SONG OF THE RIVER

SONG
OF
THE RIVER

BY

BILLY C. CLARK

DRAWINGS BY

EZRA JACK KEATS

THOMAS Y. CROWELL COMPANY
NEW YORK

Designed by EMIL SILVESTRI

Library of Congress Catalog Card No. 57-9241

Manufactured in the United States of America
by The Cornwall Press, Inc., Cornwall, N. Y.

TO MY BROTHER

JERRY CLARK

who sat beside me under the cotton bloom willows on the banks of the Big Sandy River here at our home in eastern Kentucky, fishing for the great catfish Scrapiron Jack.

SONG OF THE RIVER

CHAPTER ONE

JOHN WAS AN OLD MAN WHO LIVED ON A SHANTYBOAT.
He lived by himself, and he kept the shantyboat tied to
the willows that shaded the high mud banks at the mouth
of the Big Sandy River in eastern Kentucky. The river
was his friend, and he loved it.

Like the shantyboat, John had grown old on the river.
His gray hair matched the sun-bleached boards that
framed the boat, and age had wrinkled his skin as wind
might wrinkle the surface of water. During the past
two years his hearing had all but left him, and he had
since learned to use his eyes and read signs of the lips
to replace this loss of hearing.

The river was his greatest friend, and he always talked
to it. He knew and understood the river, and even with

his loss of hearing he felt that it had not forsaken him. He knew that he could not hear the low sound of the waves as they washed against the high mud banks, or the slow ripple of the water as it washed across the sand bars that spotted the river bed; he knew he would never again hear the wind that bent the willows on the bank until their tops sometimes brushed the surface of the water.

But still the river had not forsaken him. He used his eyes and read signs of the river as he might read a person's lips. This way he got many answers—answers that he needed. He could tell by ripples on the water if rain was coming; and if it was he knew that he must tie his shantyboat more firmly to the willows to hold against the strong current that would come to the river. Blue water was the sign of good weather and good catfishing, and catfishing was one of the ways in which he made his living. The river banks grew the young willow seedlings that he used to make his willow chairs to sell in town. The willow chairs were his main source of income. John could take the young seedlings, soak them in the river until they were soft and would not break, and then bend them into different shapes for his chairs. Small fish that he took from his fish traps sold for bait and helped buy the paint that he used to color the chairs.

John owed everything to the river. The summer brought fish, turtles, and frogs; the winter brought mink and muskrat that lived in the high mud banks; and the willows were always plentiful.

It was the first of May now, and he sat on the small deck of the shantyboat and looked out across the water.

He studied the ripples that told of rain. His many years on the river had taught him that rain always came with May. He knew that the river would swell and push water into the creek so that the fish could spawn. He knew that the river was the friend of the fish as well as his.

A warm wind lifted the tops of the willows on the bank, and John watched the tops of the low limbs brush the surface of the water. He imagined he could hear the rain crow that he had often heard on warm summer nights singing of rain from the top of one of the willows. Yet he knew that he could not and would never hear it again. Puffing his pipe and leaning back in his chair, he looked down at the river.

"River," he said, "any day now the rains will come and with the rains will come old Scrapiron Jack. He'll be coming out of that big Ohio and into the Sandy to feed. This might be my last year to catch him; I am an old man. Now you tear down the banks and build new banks in place, you wash the old willows so that new ones can grow, and you just keep going on and on, but you ain't got the power to wash the grayness from my hair or take the ache from this old body. What you have had the power to give you ain't ever denied, excepting one thing—Scrapiron Jack. And I've always reckoned that if I lived with you long enough you would even give me him. I've lived with you a long time, River. I have grown old. What do you say to that?"

John looked at the small ripples and then at the tall willows.

"Take your time, River," he said. "Take your time."

He puffed his pipe and thought of the big catfish named Scrapiron Jack. He was a great, old fish. And John could remember when the mention of his name would bring smiles to every fisherman that lived along the Big Sandy or Ohio rivers. Scrapiron Jack, a big catfish that had been hooked so many times that he carried enough scrap iron in him to be named after it. Many a fisherman had left a hook in his mouth, and John had been one. Many a fisherman had had to cut the nib on his trotline to save the line and then sit in the boat and watch the big catfish swim away. And John had been one. But he had failed to cut the nib and had lost the whole trotline.

John could remember when he first heard of Scrapiron Jack. It had been a long time ago, when he had lived on the shantyboat with his father. He could remember how his father's eyes would widen when a passing fisherman stopped to tell of someone on down the broad Ohio who had hooked the fish. His father would laugh as the man told of the fish getting away. And it made John happy, too.

Each summer during the warm nights he would sit in the joeboat and watch his father spread the soft creek minnows and crawdads along the trotline that he hoped would catch Scrapiron Jack. He could remember the night that the hard storm had come. He had sat in the joeboat and bailed out water while his father oared to the trotline, fearing that heavy brush which drifted with the swift water would lodge against the line and break it. His father had gone but a short distance along the trot when he had stopped and looked back at John.

[4]

"It's him," he had said. "Scrapiron Jack."

His father had cussed the rain and the swift water as he pulled along the trot, farther out into the river. And John had scuddled from the back of the boat, trying to keep the boat even against the current. The weight on the trot had tilted the end of the boat where his father stood and a pile of brush had hit the side, turning the boat and throwing his father into the water. The big catfish had broken water beside the boat where John sat. And as he oared the boat through the brush to his father he knew that one day he would catch the fish. One day he would find Scrapiron Jack somewhere along the trail of the willows.

He imagined he could see the big fish turn the West Virginia point, flip his large, blue tail, and glide into the Sandy. John looked again toward the willows. He knew that he must think of ways to make a living. Scrapiron Jack was a great fish, but he would not be good to eat. The fish was old and would be tough. But John did not think of money when he thought of Scrapiron Jack. Somehow he did not even like to think of killing the big fish. He had learned to respect it. But more than anything in the world he knew that he wanted to catch it. The fish had beaten him for many years. He had grown old with the fish.

Yet he knew that he must not think of the fish now. His willow chairs had been slow in selling last year, and high water had made trapping and fishing hard. Rain had kept the water swift, and hot weather late in the year had thinned the hides of the muskrat and had sprinkled the red prime hides with blue, cutting the price of the pelt in half. He had lost one trotline. Maybe to Scrapiron Jack and maybe to the current. John didn't know. But he wanted to believe it was to Scrapiron Jack. To lose a trotline to the current was waste, but to lose it to the great fish was next to catching him and was a sign that the fish was in the Big Sandy. The broken trot had made John want to catch the fish even more than ever.

He got up from the chair and stretched now. He walked to the edge of the boat and looked up the long, clay path that wound through the willows like a large, brown eel. The sun streaked through the willows, drying the early morning dew from the horseweeds that grew on both sides of the path. It was about time for the boys to be coming, John thought. The bigger boys would be in front, and little Jobe would be walking behind, carrying a large can of worms and trying to keep up.

John grinned as he bent to pull a bunch of willow limbs from the water where he had tied them to soak until they were soft enough to bend. He untied the willows and bent one. He picked up the bundle and walked back to his chair, where he could sit while he worked. He turned and looked back toward the bank.

"Hello, Mr. John."

He looked at the boys standing at the edge of the water and smiled. He looked at the willow poles over their shoulders and then up the path at little Jobe walking through the horseweeds with the can of worms.

"Well," John said, "what's this? Looks like to me

[6]

some fishermen has come to catch all the fish out of the Big Sandy."

John watched the boys grin and squint their eyes from the bright sun.

"Where would you say to fish at today, Mr. John?" the larger of the boys said.

John raised his hand and scratched his head, looking up and down the bank.

"Water's coming up a mite, Tom," John said. "Time of the white perch. Up there by the old log at the mouth of the creek would be it most likely, I'd say. What bait you bringing?"

"Red worms," Tom said.

"The river is full of minnows," John said. "Perch will take the worms if you can keep the minnows off till he finds them."

"Then maybe we can catch some minnows and use them for bait like you do on your trotline, Mr. John," Tom said.

"Might get one," the old man said. "But if you had some soft crawdads . . ." he puffed his pipe . . . "that's white perch bait."

"But we ain't got any," Tom said. "All we got is worms."

John looked up the path and watched little Jobe walk down the path with the can of worms. He watched him all the way to the boat. John looked at the bare feet and sandy hair that was long enough to blow in the wind. He knew that he had taken a great liking to Jobe. Maybe it was because Jobe was the one that always stayed to

[7]

talk. He loved to come on the shantyboat. And although John had told him the story of Scrapiron Jack many times the boy never grew tired of hearing it. He was great company to John. The little boy would sit and watch the old man weave the willow branches into chairs, and often John would let him put some of the paint on with the brush. John would always have to promise to take him along sometime when he raised the trotline. And the boy never forgot the promise. He asked every day. But Jobe was small, and the shantyboat man knew the danger of the water.

"It might be that old John has got a few," John said. " 'Course, soft crawdads are a mite scarce this early in the year. They ain't come to the edge of the creek banks to shed yet."

He puffed on his pipe and rubbed his hand over his chin. He looked toward the sun and squinted his eyes.

"Might be I could see it fitting to let you boys borrow a few," he said, "figuring you could fetch them back comes warmer weather."

Smiles came on the faces of the boys.

"We could get you a whole bucketful then, couldn't we?" Tom said.

All of the boys nodded their heads, including Jobe, who had walked up and set down the bucket of worms.

John watched the boys cross the plank to the boat, and then he walked into the cabin and came out with a wooden box in his hand. He moved one hand back and forth in the green moss that filled the box and pulled out the soft crawdads one by one.

"That ought to be enough to see if they're biting,"

he said. "Be careful around the log. The bank is steep, and the water is deep over the side."

John grinned as he watched the boys cross the plank and walk up the shore. Jobe walked behind with the bucket of worms swinging back and forth in his hand.

The old man walked back to the chair, picked up the willow branch, and sat down. As he worked he thought of the boys. They came every day. And they came to the shantyboat to find where the good fishing holes were.

John knew that they would be tired of fishing in a short while and would come to the shantyboat to sit until it was time to go up the bank. They would come to watch him weave the slender willow branches and listen to the tales of the river. They loved to hear the tales that John told them, especially the tale of Scrapiron Jack. And, for John, their smiles passed many happy hours.

CHAPTER TWO

WHILE JOHN WORKED HE FELT A MOVEMENT OF THE boat, and he turned and looked toward the board plank.

"Well, Jobe," he asked, as he watched the small boy walk over the plank to the boat, "through fishing already?"

Jobe walked up to the man, holding an empty can in his hand.

"I've come to borrow some more crawdads from you, Mr. John," he said.

"Are they biting that good?" John asked as he got up from the chair.

"You ought to see Tom's white perch," Jobe smiled, his eyes growing bigger. "I have to fish with worms because the other boys took the crawdads. And now the crawdads are all gone."

"Caught a white perch, huh," John said. "Well . . ."
John fingered through the moss . . . "we'll see if we can't
find a crawdad for you."

"Oh boy!" Jobe said. "I might catch Scrapiron Jack,
mightn't I? Then I'll say take your old white perch,
Tom."

The man looked up from the box and smiled.

"Might," he said. "It's almost time for old Scrapiron."

"I wished I was big and smart like you, Mr. John,"
Jobe said. "Then I wouldn't have to carry the bait all
the time. Why do I always have to carry it, Mr. John?"

"You are the little one, Jobe," the man said, smiling,
"and the little one always has to carry the bait. Now
when you get a little bigger. . . ."

"That's what Tom said," Jobe agreed. "But he told
me that the bigger I got, the bigger they would get. It
looks like I'm *always* going to be carrying the bait."

John laughed as he put the crawdads in the can.

"Not always," he said. "Might be when you get as
big as Tom that a smaller boy will come fishing with
you."

"He's going to carry the bait if he does," Jobe said.
"Then I can stay and fish."

"That's right," the man agreed, smiling.

"If I get Scrapiron Jack on the line I'll come to get
you, Mr. John," Jobe promised. "But I bet I won't. I
ain't smart like you. If I was I'd show that old Scrapiron."

"I'll bet you would," John said. "But I ain't too smart.
I been after him a long time and I ain't caught him yet."

"But you will," Jobe said. "You live on a boat and you

can fish all the time. I wish I could live on a boat like you. Maybe then I could talk to the river like you do."

"You might have to be on the boat a long time to get to talk to the river," the old man said. "And maybe you never would. Sometimes the river is a lonely place. It's better for you to live in town, because that's your home. I belong here on the river, because the river is my home. And right now you better get this bait back up the bank. A good fisherman stays to his line."

He watched the small boy walk up the bank, and he waved at him as the lad disappeared into the willows. He thought of what Jobe had said about wanting to live on the river. The river was a lonely place. The boy only thought of fishing and did not know what it was to be an old man alone with the river. To the boys John was the greatest fisherman on the Big Sandy River, but to the people in town he was just an old man living on a shantyboat.

John had long known many of the thoughts of people in town. He knew that few believed his tales of Scrapiron Jack. Not many people came to fish on the river any more, and the name of the great fish had died as a willow might die and be washed away by the water. John was just a crazy old fool who had spent so much time on the river that he thought he could talk to it. He was an old man searching for a fish that did not exist; an old man who peddled his fish and lived on the trail of the willows.

The thoughts of the people did not bother John. What did they know of the river, anyway? Did they know the lonely sound of the wind in the willows at night or see the gray shadows that spotted the river bed when the moon was low? Or did they know the comfort of being rocked to sleep at nights by the waves as they washed the old shantyboat back and forth? John was an old man, but he was a riverman. He knew the river because he was part of it. And he thought that one day he would walk through the streets in town with the great catfish and show the people that he was more than just an old river fool.

Now he laid the willow branch down and relighted his pipe. Then he walked to the edge of the boat to get some more limbs. He noticed Tom running down the bank. Tom was holloing something, but he was too far away to make out what it was. John walked quickly to the bank to meet the boy, thinking that one of the lads had caught a good-sized catfish and wanted him to take it off.

"Here, Tom," John said, "slow down and tell me . . . how big is it?"

"Jobe!" Tom shouted. "It's Jobe! In the water out from the log."

John started up the bank toward the log.

"Get help," he told Tom.

Then he himself swam over from the log toward the sandy-haired boy who was splashing in the current out in the river. John felt the cold water against his body and the tug of the current caused by the creek emptying into the river above the log. He was still wearing all his clothes but his shoes, and this made swimming hard. He did not even remember taking the shoes off. But he stopped now to tread water and to see where the boy was. Then he spied the lad disappearing beneath the surface. A moment later Jobe came up farther down the river.

The man's arms cramped as he swam toward the boy, and his wind was giving out. The child went under again, and now John's legs began to cramp in the cold water. He swam to the place where Jobe had gone down the last time and dived under there. The water was not deep, but the shallowness had caused an undercurrent. The undercurrent was enough to wash the boy downriver. John came up for air and then dove under again. Each time he stayed down until he thought his lungs would burst. He tried to open his eyes under the water, but it was too dark to see. He knew that the boy was gone and that he would have to use what strength was left to reach the bank. He dived once more and then started for the bank.

At the edge of the water he dug his fingers into the sand and pulled himself onto the shore. And for a while he lay there with his head over his arms.

He knew he must reach the shantyboat, where he could get his small joeboat to search for Jobe. The undercurrent of the water was swift enough to wash a small body into the broad Ohio. If the boy was to be saved he would have to be brought out of the water fast. Once in the Ohio he might never be found.

John staggered to his feet and started up the bank, following the edge of the water and holding to the willows to keep from falling.

When he got to the shantyboat there were people standing on the bank. He could see Sheriff Lemesters at the edge of the water, pointing out into the river and talking to men in two joeboats. A woman stood back from the water crying, and two other women were holding her arms.

The sheriff looked at John and walked toward him.

"How far down?" he said.

"To the bend," John said, pointing. "The water is swift underneath."

"How swift?" Sheriff Lemesters said.

"Swift enough to carry a body," John said, breathing hard.

"Swift enough for him to be in the Ohio?" Sheriff Lemesters said.

John lowered his head and wiped his face.

"Unless he was lodged," he said.

"You better get out of them wet clothes and into something dry," Sheriff Lemesters said. "Not much you can do."

"I got a boat," John said. "And I know the river. I know where he could snag if he was washed in close. I want to look for the boy, Sheriff. I felt awful close to him."

"How much chance has he got of snagging, John?" Sheriff Lemesters asked.

"Well . . ." John said. "Not much, I reckon, but it's a chance."

"You go change your clothes, John," Sheriff Lemesters said. "You done your best. Not many your age would do that."

John walked toward the boat and in front of the woman who was crying. He looked into her face.

"You killed him!" she said. "You killed my boy!"

She grabbed for John, and the two women holding her pulled her back.

"You killed him!" she screamed. "You and your fool tales of the river. Teaching boys that the water won't hurt them. You killed Jobe!"

She grabbed for him again and then fell to the sand and cried.

John walked onto the boat and into the cabin. He dried his face and tried to think. Everything had happened so fast. One minute Jobe had been on the boat and the next he was in the water being swept by the current. I could have kept him here, John thought, as he pulled off the wet clothes. But how could he have known that Jobe would fall into the water? He thought of what the woman had said. "How," he said aloud, "have I killed the boy? How have I confused his mind with tales of the river?"

John sat down and put his face in his hands. There *was* a fish named Scrapiron Jack, he told himself. And he had never lied to the boy. He had taught him to love the river. Maybe this was wrong. But he himself had never learned fear of the river, and he had seen people drown before. All he knew was that he loved Jobe. He had fallen into the water and been swept away by the current. John had done all he could. Why had the woman screamed and accused him?

He changed his clothes and walked out onto the deck of the shantyboat. The people were gone. Some were probably farther down the bank watching the dragging. John looked down the river trying to see if he could

locate one of the joeboats. He looked close to the willows that hung over the bank, hoping that he might see one of the boats working in close to the shore. But he could see nothing but willows and water. And he knew that the boats must be dragging the Ohio. He walked over to the chair and sat down.

The sun set behind the willows, and a strong wind rippled the water. John watched the shadows move along the shore, farther and farther out into the river. It would soon be dark. The search would soon be over. The boy was gone. John knew that. The only hope now was to find his body so that he might be buried. If the body was not found the fish would get it. John had seen a body eaten by fish before. That had happened a long time ago, but he had never forgotten. It was the body of a man who had been snagged on a trotline below the mouth of the Big Sandy. He had seen the people gather on the bank, and he had walked down. The flesh had been torn; and the whole body bobbed up and down in the water, washing in and out on the rope that was tied to one arm. The rope had cut through the soft flesh, and John could see the bone. The flesh looked bloated and chalky.

And now he thought of Jobe being tied by a rope to a willow, and tears came to his eyes. He looked down at the water.

"I thought you was my friend, River," he said. "You took the boy, not me. I wouldn't hurt anyone. I am an old man, a lonely old man. Why did you take the boy, River? Answer me that."

John looked at the ripples on the water and wiped his eyes again.

"You won't answer, will you, River?" he said. "Maybe you can't. Maybe there is some things, like me, you just don't know. Maybe it was the will of the Lord. But why did it have to be Jobe? Why couldn't you have took me? I am old, with just a few years to go. Nothing left in me but a little fishing, and nobody would care."

John sat in the chair until the wind came up harder. The wind was cold, and he felt a few drops of rain. He got up from the chair and walked into the cabin. He built a small fire in the stove and lit his pipe. John felt tired and he lay down on the small cot. He could feel the movement of the boat on the water.

CHAPTER THREE

DURING THE NIGHT THE WIND BECAME STRONGER, AND THE whitecaps on the water rocked the boat. John sat up and lit his pipe. He walked to the door and looked out into the dark. The rain beat against the side of the boat. This was the rain that he knew would come. It was a little early this year. He could not see the water, but by daylight it would be muddy and swift. The Big Sandy was not a large stream; even a little water caused it to swell. It would be useless to drag for the boy. The body would come to the surface in nine days and then, if it was not spotted, it would go down forever.

John walked back into the cabin and poked some wood on the fire. Then he sat down in the chair to wait for daylight. He knew that he could not sleep. The sleep before had come because of tiredness. His arms and legs were still cramped, and they were sore from the swim in the water. With daylight there would be lots of work to do. He knew that he would have to set his trotline because the rains would bring Scrapiron Jack.

Daylight came slowly. John watched it sift over the tops of the willows and spread across the water through a heavy rain. He looked at the muddy water. He watched it swirl along the bank, knocking loose chunks of the bank mud. The willows were straightening in the strong wind. There was nothing John could do but wait for the rain to slack.

He walked back in the cabin with a few willow branches and began to bend them into shape. He had decided to make a willow rocker this time, and he knew that it would take a lot of work. But a rocker would be apt to bring more money, and he had sold one last year. Reverend Crites had bought the last one. Reverend Crites had bought three chairs from him last year. And that had been all that John had sold.

Reverend Crites was a good man, and he always came to see the old fisherman when he went to town to sell the chairs. He never passed him on the streets without asking how he was and if he had ever landed the big fish. He never laughed when John told him that he was still trying.

The three chairs had helped to buy a new line and food. And with the money John had made from his turtles, frogs, and hides, he had got through the cold winter.

The rain did not stop now. Sometimes it slacked; but

from the looks of the heavy black clouds in the sky, John knew that he would not be able to make it to his trotline, which should be reset and baited.

The rain came in waves, and the river began to swell. Heavy brush drifted in the water, and small piles began to lodge against the front of the shantyboat. John walked out into the rain and tore the brush loose. He knew that the small piles would soon become larger and the pressure of the water against them could break the rope that held the shantyboat. Even if they didn't tear the boat loose, when the river quieted and fell it would leave the brush to be carried away by hand.

The rain fell all day, and darkness came early. The dark clouds blackened the sky, and streaks of lightning lit up the river. Although John could not hear, he thought that he could feel the loud thunder that rolled along the surface of the water. He knew that he could not make it to the trotline. Maybe he would not even have a line by the time he was able to get to the snag where it was tied. The brush was still heavy on the water, and he knew that there was brush floating underneath. He knew that logs, half-soaked with water, drifted under the surface. Some of them rolled along the bottom and others floated closer to the top. Either was apt to catch a trotline. If one snagged on a line the pressure of the water and the weight of the log could break a strong line. It would break his line. The line had been used one summer and late fall and had been dried but one time. It was a cloth line, which was not the best, but it was as good as John could afford.

He finished the frame of the chair now before he lay

down. Then once again he started to get up and work into the night because he could not sleep. He knew if he lay long enough that sleep would come. He could remember how he used to lie awake when he was a boy and his father was living. He used to think that daylight would never come. He would lie awake thinking of the trotline that he and his father had baited earlier in the day and of all the fish that they would be taking from it. But after a while he learned that daylight always came. And most times it caught him asleep, and his father had to wake him.

Daylight came now. John walked to the door and looked out. The rain had turned to a fine mist. John walked out and looked at the river. It was muddy but not too swift. The Big Sandy was quick to rise, but it fell just as fast once the rains stopped. A heavy rain could swell the river one night, and by the end of the following day the river would be running out. Everything really depended on the Ohio. And it took a lot of water to make the Ohio back into the Sandy. Silt settled fast in the Big Sandy, and the water cleared fast.

John took a can and bailed the water that had fallen in the joeboat, and then he walked back into the cabin. He brought out the box of crawdads and placed them in the floor of the joeboat. There would not be much bait. And it would take time for the river to get in shape so that he could find more. He could get plenty of worms, but worms were not too good after a rain. Maybe because the rains washed so many worms from the banks. Anyway, crawdads and minnows were better bait. He thought that he could save what few crawdads he had for the hooks farther out and use worms for the close ones.

John stepped into the boat and started upriver, staying out from the bank to avoid the current caused by the creek.

The mist began to clear, and the sun broke over the willows. The heat from the sun felt good. The water was muddy, but it was not too rough. He knew that it would clear fast. The black clouds had left the sky, and there was no sign of more rain.

Sand bars that spotted the river bed began to stick above the water; and the killdees walked along the edge of the sand, looking for minnows in close. John looked at the brown-spotted bird that bobbed its tail up and down as it walked on land. The bird had always looked funny to John, like it was off balance. But this was only when it was on land. In the air it was smooth and fast. A killdee could swoop down out of the air to the surface of the water and scoop up a minnow without touching its feathers. Its eyes were keen. The bird was a friend to a fisherman, for it would lead him to the minnow schools. John thought that to the bird the air was like the river was to the fish.

Around a bend above the creek he turned the boat toward the bank. He laid one of the oars aside and used the other to paddle up close to a large, brown snag that was sticking out of the water a few feet from shore. The snag had at one time been a large willow tree. John took hold of it, bent down, and stuck his arm into the water in front. He pulled up the rope trotline. The line swung downriver with the current because the trot had been broken. How far out he did not know. He cut the line from the snag, and while the boat drifted with the current he wound in the line.

John figured the line to be broken about a third of the way out. Several hooks he passed were bent straight. This was the sign of brush that had caught on the trot. The line was too short for a trotline; maybe a few turtle lines could be made from it. Few hooks were left because John had learned long ago to start his nibs out where the water was the deepest. Small fish stripped hooks that were closest to the bank and large fish took the hooks where the water was the deepest. As a rule, small fish worked the edge of banks and the large ones worked the deep water.

John tied the joeboat to the shanty and carried the line and bait into the cabin. Turtle hooks would not catch Scrapiron Jack, he thought, as he laid the line beside the stove. The skimpy bait had turned out to be more than enough.

John walked out onto the small deck and crossed the plank to the shore. He stopped and looked up the clay path. And as he looked he felt a loneliness inside him. He missed the boys. He did not think that they would be coming today. But they might come tomorrow, he thought, as he cut some of the low-hanging willow limbs.

He took the bundle of limbs and walked back to the boat. He tied the bundle with a piece of rope and lowered them over the side into the water. Then he lit his pipe and sat down in the chair.

He sat for a long time looking up the clay path. At every movement in the willows he rose from the chair and tried to see through the horseweeds shading the path. Each time it was only the wind or a bird that moved in the willows trying to see a young grasshopper in the horseweed patch.

Maybe the boys will never come, John thought, puffing hard on his pipe. But the boys would know that it was not him that took Jobe; they would know it was the river. And then he thought of the river without the boys, and for the first time he felt the loneliness of the water. He had always lived alone on the river, in the shantyboat, but the boys had always come down the bank each day and talked to him. They didn't come much during the winter; but John was on the creeks more during trapping season, and nearly every day one of the boys would be running along the bank watching him make his sets.

John walked around to the back of the boat now and picked up two pieces of flat board. He had pulled them from the drift that had lodged against the boat during the storm. He could use these boards to carve rockers for the rocking chair he was making. The carving would keep him busy until the willow limbs were soaked enough to bend into shape. The boards were still wet, and John laid them on the front of the boat to dry in the sun. Then he walked into the cabin.

John looked at the piece of line lying by the stove. He puffed his pipe and rubbed his hand over his chin. That line would have to be used again. It was too short, but he did not have the money for a new one. He did not know how long it would take him to get the money. He could finish the rocking chair in a week by working late at nights, but there was no way of telling when somebody would buy it.

There were always the same people in Catlettsville, and John knew them all by face and name. Few strangers were seen except when they were passing through. He had carried his chairs to town for many years now, and it was not often that he sold more than two or three a summer. The price of the chairs had always been much cheaper than was justified by the work it took to make them.

Yes, the line was short; but there was one way he could reach the water with it, and that was to float it with jugs.

He picked up the rope and walked out on the deck. He unwound the line and measured it again. The line could hold about twenty nibs if the nibs were scattered close along the line. Line would have to be left open on both ends so that he could tie on the jugs. He could anchor the jugs with smaller line because he knew that there would be no pressure on the sinkers. Then the jugs could float on the water, and by watching the jugs he could tell when the line had taken a fish. Even a fish as large as Scrapiron Jack could not hold the jugs under the water for long, and if the line was put out a little above the shantyboat it could be watched during the day from the boat. But Scrapiron Jack could easily pull the line to snags where he could twist and break it.

John rewound the line and placed it in the joeboat. Then he walked to the cabin and got his bait and two jugs. The chance of catching many fish on the line was slim, but it was still a chance. And every year that he had lived on the boat with his father he had had a line in the water. But the line will not stay long, he thought, as he stretched it out along the water. It would stay only long enough for him to get a good long trotline in by the snag upriver. Then he could cut this line and make turtle lines from it.

John baited the line with worms and soft crawdads and then scuddled back to the boat. When he passed the creek he turned his head. It had been here that Jobe had fallen into the water. John could not yet believe that the boy was gone. And then he wondered if he had been found. John would be going to town in a day or two, and then he would know. Or maybe some of the boys would be coming to the river tomorrow, and they would tell him. When they came to ask about the fishing holes he could find out.

John scuddled the joeboat to the shanty and tied onto the tiepost. He took what bait was left and put it inside the cabin. Then he walked back out on the deck and sat down in the chair.

He sat in the chair and carved on the rockers until darkness settled over the river. Dark clouds hid the tops of the willows, and a wind rippled the water. John knew that there would be more rain. The rain would come sometime during the night. The wind was not too strong, and there was a good chance that much of the rain would move up Sandy. The clouds were moving in the sky toward the land that lay beyond the West Virginia point.

John walked into the cabin and lay down on the cot. He could feel the steady knock of the joeboat against the side of the shanty, and he could feel the movement of the water.

CHAPTER FOUR

THE RAIN HAD BEEN LIGHT, AND BY THE TIME JOHN WAS
up, the deck of the shantyboat had dried. He fixed his
breakfast and stepped out into the joeboat. He bailed
water from the boat and then scuddled to the jugs. He
could see the far jug bobbing up and down in the water,
and he knew that the line held a fish.

John took two small catfish from it and rebaited. On
his way back to the shantyboat he stopped at the mouth
of the creek, dropped two small minnow traps into the
water, and tied them to a willow limb hanging low to
the creek. He sat in the boat looking at the log and then
paddled back to the shanty.

John spent the day making turtle lines. He made the
lines about three feet long and tied an extra-large hook

to one end. The other end he knotted to keep the line from unraveling. After he had fixed as many as he could keep baited, he worked on the rocking chair.

When the sun went down he started upriver in the joeboat. He rowed to the mouth of the creek and raised the minnow traps. Both traps were heavy with minnows. He took a few from the traps and dropped them back into the water. Then he paddled out to the jugs.

All of the hooks on the line were stripped, and John knew this was because the line had drifted close to the West Virginia bank in next to a sand bar. Small fish had nibbled at the bait until the hooks were bare. And after he had rebaited he pulled the line farther out into the river and tied on heavier sinkers. Then he headed the boat toward the Kentucky side.

John stopped at snags that were out in the water on that side of the river and began to set his turtle hooks. He worked along the bank downriver toward the shanty-boat, tying a line to each snag he passed and putting a piece of liver on the hook. The snags were the homes of the turtles, and liver was the bait they liked best. Turtles were easy to sell, and they brought better money than fish.

This side of the creek John tied his last turtle line, thinking that this set would probably snag the first turtle. He tied the line under the roots of a large willow growing at the edge of the water. The river had hollowed the dirt beneath the roots and ran about two feet deep under them.

As John rowed past the creek he thought of Jobe and the boys. He looked at the big log that had been bedded in the mud near the creek many years ago. This was the log that Jobe had fallen from; it was the fishing place of the boys. They had worn the weeds and grass from the top of the log where they had sat and fished over the side. Again today the boys had not come. Maybe they knew the river was still a bit heavy with dirt, John thought. Tomorrow the river would be clearer—clear enough to fish.

The water cleared next day, but still the boys did not come. John had watched the path up the bank until he had grown tired. Three days now had passed since the accident. And during the three days John had done a lot of thinking. He did not believe that the boys would ever come again to the shantyboat. He did not think it was the boys' fault. Yet he did not believe they would come. If they were coming they would have been to the river before now. After this, John thought, there would be just himself and the river. And he thought that maybe it was best this way—to be alone with just the river. There would be nothing to worry about except his lines and boat and the little money that he needed to live on.

What people thought did not matter to John, but he worried over what they might have told the boys to make them keep away from the river and the boat. He knew that, to many in town, he had long carried the nickname "Scrapiron John"; but he did not care. One day he thought that they would see. And if they didn't then he still wouldn't mind. As long as he knew that old fish was in the river he would have his line waiting.

John knew that the people could not understand why an old man would live alone all these years on the river in a shantyboat pieced together with driftwood. Sometimes it had been hard for him to understand himself. But in the river he found his answer. He loved the river because it had been all he had ever known, and he had nothing to regret. His schooling had been in the ways of the water. John grinned as he thought. Here he was an old man, and he could not even write his name. But on the river he did not have to write his name.

He knew that some people laughed at the clothes he wore when he went to town, but he thought he would rather have a good trotline than a suit of clothes. He had no need for a suit. His life was the river, and his ambition was to catch Scrapiron Jack before he died. To some people, John knew, this would be a simple wish; but to him it was a wish that his greatest friend, the river, had denied. At least, the river had denied it to him so far, and he was now an old man.

John looked at the willow chair as he stroked the paint brush over it. He thought that this was the best chair he had ever made. The chair had taken a lot of time and work. If it sold he planned to buy a new trotline—a good trotline. Scrapiron Jack would be feeding in the Big Sandy until late fall.

When darkness came, John took his flashlight and walked to the creek. Although he could no longer hear the frogs, he knew that some should be sitting along the warmer water of the creek. He knew that the ones he would find would be sitting at the very edge of the water with only their noses sticking out. They would sit this way until the weather was warm. Frogs sold cheap, but they were easy to sell.

John moved slowly up the creek, walking the bank. Later in the year he would wade the stream, where he would be able to see better; but right now the least ripple of water would cause the frogs to go under. Later in the year they would sit high on the bank.

John walked the creek until the wind was up and then he started back. He had caught six nice frogs, the only big ones he had seen. A few little frogs had been sitting out on brush piles, but John left them there to grow.

He set the frogs on the deck of the shantyboat now and walked into the cabin. In the morning he would take the frogs to town with the rocking chair, and with luck he might be bringing a new trotline back to the river.

John walked out on the deck and sat down in the chair. He looked across the water. The wind had quieted and the night was clear. He lit his pipe and looked toward the clay path.

CHAPTER FIVE

JOHN WAS ON THE WATER AT DAYBREAK, RAISING THE JUG-line. He baited the hooks on the raise and took one small mudcat from the last hook. Then he put the fish back in the water and watched it swim away. He rowed to the Kentucky bank and looked at the turtle lines on the way back to the boat. Not a line had been touched, but neither had the bait. And this was one thing that John liked about fishing for turtles: large chunks of liver were too big to be stolen by minnows that swam around the snags at night. Either he caught a turtle or he kept the bait.

It will be good, he thought, as he rowed past the creek, to get a big line in the river. This was the shortest line he had ever had in the water at this time of year. Often

SONG OF THE RIVER

during the winter he ran short lines; large fish came close to the bank during the cold weather to get in the warmth of the sun and to work the shoals.

John tied the boat to the shanty and walked into the cabin. He washed his face and hands and brushed his clothes. Then he took the frogs and the chair and walked across the plank to the shore.

It seemed a long way up the path. The horseweeds, still wet from the morning dew, swayed over the path; they brushed against John's clothes, rubbing water on them. John turned off the path onto the brick road that followed the top of the riverbank. He nodded his head at several men sitting on a wooden bench in front of a brick building at the corner of the road and turned the corner toward the town's main street. He stopped in front of a small restaurant set between the river road and the main street, and walked in.

There were two men sitting at the counter. One of them John knew; the other he did not.

"Got some frogs, Bert," John said, as he walked over to the counter and put down the frogs and chair.

The man behind the counter looked up at John. Then he looked at the two men.

"Cold yet for frogs, ain't it?" he said. "Where'd you find them?"

One of the men at the counter set his coffee cup down and looked toward the sack. Then he looked up at John.

"Don't you know, Bert?" he said. "The river's told old Scrapiron where they was. Didn't they, Scrapiron? He's the only man can catch frogs this time of year and weather."

The man turned his head and said something to the stranger beside him, and John saw the man laugh.

"Six good frogs, Bert," John said. "Let you have them cheap."

"Give you fifty cents for the lot," Bert said. "Never get calls for frogs. Most folks catch their own when the weather is right."

John looked at the sack and lifted it off the floor. Then he set it back down.

"Ought to be worth a dollar," he said.

Even at a dollar he knew he was giving the frogs away. He had seen the time when two frogs would bring a dollar.

"Fifty cents for the lot," Bert said. "Take it or leave it."

John looked at the sack again. He needed the money. He lifted the sack and handed them across the counter.

"And you clean 'em," Bert said. "You can use the room in the back."

"Won't charge 'im for the room, will you Bert?" the man at the counter said, and laughed.

John walked to the back room and cleaned the frogs. Bert handed him the fifty cents and looked at the size of the frogs. John folded the sack and stuck it in his pocket.

"Have they found the boy yet, Bert?" John asked, bending over the counter.

"Two days ago," Bert said. "Snagged on a trotline down the Ohio. Tore up pretty bad, I hear. They buried him yesterday. Last one to see 'im alive, wasn't you, Scrapiron?"

"Reckon," John said. "Tried to get to him but the water was swift. Had to swim to the bank."

"Water washes scum to the bank," the man at the counter said. John knew that the man did not know he heard. But his eyes were keen, and the words had been easy to make out. He picked up the chair.

"Thanks, Bert," he said.

"Might take some more frogs later on," Bert said. "See how I do on these. Stop from time to time."

John walked out the door and headed for the main street. He stopped at the corner and set the rocking chair down. Then he lit his pipe and leaned up against the side of the brick building on the corner. The sun was hot, and John took off his broad-rimmed hat and wiped his forehead. He looked down at the chair. The sun shining on the paint made the chair look pretty, he thought. It ought to sell.

CHAPTER SIX

THE WILLOWS FLOWERED, AND THE FUZZY, WHITE blooms fell. John watched them hug the edge of the water and drift with the slow current downriver. The blooms showed that May was ending. Almost a month, and the chair had not sold. John looked at the long paths of willow blooms and puffed his pipe. Many people did not know that the willow had a bloom, he thought. And to many it was not a pretty flower. But to him it was. Not many flowers bloomed along the river, and the bloom of the willows almost stood alone. John always looked forward to seeing them. It was pretty to look through the willows on a warm summer night and see the white blooms like small puffs of smoke against a blue sky.

Small minnows came to the surface of the water now and struck at the blooms as they fell on the water. Small circles formed wherever the minnows broke surface, and the small rings would wash toward the bank and disappear. It would not be long now until almost all of the minnows would disappear from the river. Some would grow to a larger size; many would be eaten by the larger fish; and many would swim up the shallow water of the creeks.

The creeks were always heavy with minnows. John knew that even during the cold winter days he could break the ice that formed on top of the water and scoop out a minnow to use for a mink set.

He looked at the rocking chair he had made almost a month ago. Beside it sat two smaller chairs that he had also made during that time. None of the chairs had sold. One man had stopped to look at them yesterday and John had thought that he was going to buy, but he had only complimented him on his craftsmanship and walked on.

Still John realized that the summer was just beginning and he would have lots of time in which to sell the chairs. He thought that if he only had a good line in the water he would not mind the wait too much. At least he would stand a chance of catching the big catfish. He knew that he would never catch old Scrapiron on the small jugtrot. For one thing it was too close to the surface of the water; and even if the fish was caught the line would be easy to pull. The first snag that the fish hit to hold the line solid would break it like sewing thread.

John thought of Mr. Hardler, who owned the small

hardware store in town. He had bought a lot of fishing stuff there, and Mr. Hardler was his friend. He knew that the merchant would let him have the trotline if he asked for it. He knew that he could pay for it later.

But John had always remembered the words of his father: "First you ask and then you beg." John had lived a long time by himself, and during that time he had done without many things that he needed; but he had never asked for a thing he had not paid for. He had learned to wait. Sometimes the waiting was hard and most times the things that he had waited for never came, and still he had not asked.

He had waited many years for Scrapiron Jack. Each summer he had expected to catch the great catfish, and he had watched the leaves fall from the trees and the brown banks turn white with snow. Puffing his pipe, he would be thinking of the coming summer. John thought that it was Scrapiron, more than anything else, that had taught him to wait.

The boys no longer came to the river. They no longer came to ask about the fishing holes or watch John weave his fish traps or willow chairs. He was alone with the river. And during the past trips to town he had been able to learn some of the reasons. At first he had not be-lieved the things he heard. And then he had seen Tom on his last trip to town. He had motioned for Tom to come over to where he was sitting. Tom had just looked at him across the street and walked away. Then he had known why many of the boys he had seen at the river had turned away when he passed. John had heard that they had been warned to stay away from the shantyboat.... "Stay away from the old man living on the river with evil powers because he might drag you into the water like he did Jobe."

"Ain't that somethin'?" a drunk had said to John. "My old woman tells our boy that if he don't mind what she says you're goin' to git 'im, Scrapiron. Ain't that somethin'? Afraid of an old man like you."

John had tried to force a smile, but all day he had thought of what the drunk had said. He wondered what there was for the boys to be afraid of. He had done nothing. He had swum after Jobe until he had to head for shore to save his own life, and now he was being accused of killing the boy. He could still see the woman reaching for him and crying. Maybe it would have been better, he thought, if the river had taken him. But he was still here, and as long as he was he knew that he would live the only life he had ever known. He could understand the thoughts of the river, but people puzzled him. He felt lucky to live on the shantyboat.

There was one thing that John did know, from now on it would be just him. He would never let anyone or anything take his thought from the river. One day he would show the boys that he was not lying to them. He would carry Scrapiron Jack through the streets in town.

Still he did not blame the boys at all. A young boy would believe almost anything he was told until he was big enough to know better. John could remember how his own father had told him that a waterdog walked along the bottom of the river barking like a dog. He had believed this. And then one day he had caught a waterdog and found that what his father had told him was not true. It had very small legs; its skin was like a catfish, and it did not bark like a dog or walk; it swam.

One day the boys would learn about the old man and the shantyboat just as he had learned about the water-dog. They would learn that he was good and loved them and meant no harm. And if they learned the power and beauty of the river they would know why he had lived on the shantyboat.

CHAPTER SEVEN

MAY HAD ENDED AND JUNE HAD STARTED. AND STILL THE chairs had not sold. John could not sell enough frogs or fish at one time to buy the trotline. He had to use what money he made to live on. And he would have to start saving for the winter. He began to spend more time on the water, and June seemed to be going faster than May. There had not been many fishermen on the river. The water had stayed bad most of the summer. Heavy rains had kept the river swollen and full of brush. His own small line had been caught by brush and broken, and he had had to shorten it again and again.

Summer would soon be ending, and John knew that he must get ready for the trapping season. He needed a few more traps. Signs in the sky told him that it would be a cold winter, coming early. The pelts would be good, and with luck on the trap line he could make some money. Trapping was not like fishing; traps could be bought one at a time and did not cost much. But a line had to be bought all at once.

Some fishermen stopped at the shantyboat the last of June and bought some bait. They said that they were camped several miles up Sandy and had hooked a great catfish. John smiled when they told of the fish getting away. As they described it he knew that they were talking about old Scrapiron, and he was happy to know that the old fish was in the Big Sandy. He knew that if Scrapiron had been hooked that far upriver he must be staying late to feed in the small stream. Scrapiron should be coming down with the late raise. With a good line in the water John knew he might be able to hook him. Once into the Ohio, Scrapiron would not be back until spring. And if he was caught in the Ohio he would never be back.

Once again John took his chairs to town and set them in the same place on the corner. Not many people were on the streets that day. A strong wind was blowing up, and John cupped his hand to light his pipe. He looked up at the man standing in front of him.

"Morning, John," the man said.

"Morning, Reverent," John said, puffing on his pipe to keep it lit.

"See you still got the chairs."

"Yep," John said, "still got the three."

The preacher walked over to the chairs and ran his

hand across the top of the rocker. Then he looked at John.

"Tell me, John," he said, "have you sold any chairs this year?"

The old man fumbled with his pipe and then rubbed his hands on his pants.

"Well . . . not yet I ain't," he said. "But I ain't been coming up the bank too often, Reverent. Got a lot of work to do fixing the boat, fishing and all, you know. Made these chairs during my spare time."

"Lot of work here, John," Reverend Crites said. "Beautiful chairs. . . . I don't see how you do it with nothing but those willows."

John smiled and looked at the chairs.

"Took my time on the rocker," he said. "Just like the one you bought last year."

"Yes, it is," Reverend Crites said. "I was just noticing that. How is fishing this year, John?"

"Water's been bad," John said, looking at the small black clouds that had formed in the sky. "But I been catching a few from day to day."

"Any luck on the big one?"

"No. But you know what, Reverent . . . he's in the river. And he ought to come down late this fall."

The preacher looked at John and smiled.

"Bet you got your line waiting," he said.

John looked at Reverend Crites and then walked over to the chairs. He pulled a piece of loose bark off one of them.

"Lost my line to high water," he said, studying the

chairs. "Fixing to buy a new one . . . one maybe that I can stretch from bank to bank."

"You ought to have a line in the water, John," the preacher said. "I guess to you that line is like my Bible is to me, in one sense anyway."

He put his hand on the rocker.

"I was telling Mrs. Crites yesterday that I thought I saw you with one of these rockers like she bought last year. She asked me to stop and see. She is awful proud of the one she's got. If I don't take this one before someone else buys it I don't reckon I would be able to *go* home. How much is it, John?"

John looked at the chair and then at Reverend Crites. He watched the preacher rubbing his hand over the back of the rocker.

"Reverent . . . I . . . ." John took his eyes from the rocker and looked down at the sidewalk.

"What is it, John?"

"Well. . . . It's just that I'm figuring you don't really *need* the chair."

"Just a minute, John. I know a good buy when I see one."

"Things is going pretty good," John said. "I been selling frogs 'bout as fast as I catch them."

"John," the preacher said, "I couldn't tell you how to set a trotline—how to bait just so the fish would take it, and just where on the river they would take it—now could I?"

John looked at Reverend Crites and smiled.

"Don't reckon you could," he said. "The river is my home."

"Then, for the same reason, you can't tell me how many chairs I want, where to set them in the house, and what kind to buy—now could you, John?" Reverend Crites asked gently. "And my house is *my* home."

John laughed. "Reckon you're right," he said.

"Now then," the preacher said, "how much is the rocking chair?"

" 'Bout three dollars."

"Tell you what. I'll give you three-fifty, and you can take it over to the house for me and tell Mrs. Crites I sent it."

John lit his pipe and folded the money and put it in his pocket.

"Thank you, Reverent," he said. "I won't forget."

"I'm getting the bargain, John."

John picked up the chairs and started down the road.

He took the rocker to Mrs. Crites and then walked back to the shantyboat. He emptied some change from a small jar where he had been saving and walked back up the path, leaving the two smaller chairs inside the cabin. He figured that he had about enough money for a good line, a few extra hooks, and maybe a ball of stag-gon for nibs. He thought that he could sell the other chairs and put the money back in the jar. With a good line in the river, waiting wouldn't be so bad.

John walked into the small hardware store and headed for the counter where the fishing equipment was kept. There he saw two large spools of line. John looked at one of them. It was a different type of line from any he had ever used. He unwound a piece of the cord and studied it closely. He thought that was the finest line he had ever seen. A small wire ran through the center and the outside was slick, hard cloth. A trotline like this would last forever, he thought. Just then the owner came from behind the other counter and walked toward him.

"Well, John," Mr. Hardler said, "you're late coming this year. I was afraid something might have happened to you. Fine cord you got there in your hand."

John pulled the line back and forth through his palm and asked, "How much would, say, a long trot cost?"

"That depends on how long, John. How far was you fixing to stretch?"

"Maybe clear across the Sandy."

Mr. Hardler turned toward the front of the store, and John looked up. A man had walked through the door and stopped just inside.

"Just a minute, John," Mr. Hardler said, walking toward the other customer.

When the man turned around John could see who he was. "Still after him, are you, Scrapiron?" the man said.

"He ought to be awful big by now. Wait a while and his fins will give him away. You can save your money then."

John looked back at the line and waited for Mr. Hardler to finish his business with this chatterbox.

"Now, John," the proprietor said when the man had left, "let's see . . . Sandy's about a hundred yards wide most times, I'd say, right here at the mouth. Cord is three cents a foot. That would mean about . . ." Mr. Hardler rubbed his hand over his chin . . . "that would be three-hundred foot times three."

John looked at the shiny wire in the center of the line. "How much would that come to?" he asked. "Need some staggon and a few hooks, too."

Mr. Hardler pulled a pencil from behind his ear and scribbled on top of a piece of paper that was pushed partway under the glass on top of the small counter.

"Nine dollars for the line," he said. " 'Course, you know, John . . . this line wasn't exactly made for trotlines. This cord on the other spool is cheaper."

John looked at the cloth line on the other spool. It was not a bad line, he could see that. He had used it before. He knew that if he took this cheaper line from the water several times a year it would last a long spell.

"Reckon I want about that much of this line," he said, pointing to the cheaper kind.

John walked to the back counter and waited for Mr. Hardler to measure the cord. And then he handed him the money, after he had used up the change in hooks and staggon. He walked from the store and turned around the building toward the river.

He had bought enough line to reach a long way, he thought, and it was a good line. John opened the sack and examined his purchase. He stopped on top of the bank. There was a shiny wire sticking from the end of the line and the cord was smooth. Mr. Hardler had made a mistake, he thought, and had given him the wrong line. John turned and walked back to the store.

He pulled the line from the sack and walked toward the back counter.

"Forget something, John?" Mr. Hardler asked quietly.

"It's about this line," he said, fingering the shiny wire that stuck from the end.

"Now about that line, John, you can just . . ."

"But Mr. Hardler, I . . ."

"I know," Mr. Hardler said. "But you see, John, 'bout this time every year I get a taste for a big mess of frogs. I been too busy in the store to get out this year, so I figure you might be able to help me out." Mr. Hardler scratched his head. "Reckon I clear forgot to ask you about the frogs. Glad you come back."

John pushed the cord back into the sack.

"I won't forget, Mr. Hardler," he said.

"Oh . . . just one thing, John. You know how Mrs. Hardler is about me eating frogs. Reckon you could sneak them to me?"

John nodded his head and walked out of the store, turning toward the river.

CHAPTER EIGHT

JOHN WORKED UNTIL AFTER DARK FIXING THE NEW NIBS for the trotline, and when he could no longer see on the small deck he walked into the cabin and worked by the lantern. He figured that the line would hold about a hundred nibs if they were spaced right across the line. He made the nibs about two feet long and tied each end in a double knot; one of the ends he looped for the hook. When he finished a nib he held it close to the lantern and looked at the new shiny hook sticking through the small loop. He knew he would have to finish the nibs before he went to bed. Tomorrow he would be very busy. It was a long, hard job, stretching a new trot and tying the hooks. Then, too, he would have to get the bait, soft crawdads and minnows.

Before dark he had moved his minnow traps farther up the creek to the deep holes shaded by willow and maple. This way he was sure to catch soft creek minnows instead of the river shiners, and he should catch more. Not many shiners were left in the river now, and small fish were moving upcreek. The crawdads would have to be seined. Crawdads did not go in the minnow traps like the minnows did. But they could be caught in a seine, under brush and rocks. Not many soft crawdads could be caught, but John knew that by peeling the hard shells from the others he could get the white, soft meat that fish would take.

He pulled the joeboat into the mouth of the creek as daylight broke over the willows. On the way to the minnow traps he seined enough crawdads to find out if the fish were biting on them. Most of the hooks could take minnows; and then, if he found that the crawdads took the fish on the first raise, he could spend a day seining.

Both of the minnow traps were heavy with minnows. John put the crawdads in the traps to hold until the line was set and then lowered the traps into the water again. The minnow traps were heavy; if they had not been, John would have had to seine. Now he could take more time with the trotline and come for the bait when he was ready.

He walked back to the joeboat and rowed to the large snag above the creek.

John made a few wraps with the line around the snag and tied it; then he moved toward the West Virginia point, letting the line unravel as he went. After the stretch would come the nibs; and next, the bait.

A few feet from the West Virginia side John stopped and filled his pipe. He studied the bank and the small channel. He looked back toward the Kentucky side and smiled. The old willow snag looked small from where he was sitting; the trot was a long one. He thought that it would be better not to tie to both banks. A few feet off shore would be better for this end, so the line could give with the current or a log that might drift into it—or with the big catfish, if he was hooked.

John pulled the boat to the bank and tied it to a willow. He stepped out of the boat with the end of the trot and fastened it to the boat rope. Then he walked up the bank looking for a rock to use as a sinker.

He found a large hunk of gravel that was wider on both ends than it was in the middle. And thinking that the line could be tied around this rock, he carried it back to the boat. He tied it from the bank and then placed it on the floor of the joeboat.

The line did not have to be stretched this time and John let it sink under the water. The slow-moving current would hold the line tight so that he could measure the distance between nibs. The line disappeared and John started for the Kentucky side.

The sun began to set across the tops of the willows as he pulled the line upriver for the last time to stretch. The work was done now, and there was nothing to do but wait. He had a good line, good bait; the rest was up to the river.

He could not keep the trotline baited. Gars had begun to move in the water, clipping away the bodies of the small creek minnows and leaving only the heads to show where they had robbed the hook. Gars rarely ran this late in the year, but heavy water could have caused it. For almost a week they had stolen the bait as fast as John could get it on. At times he had seen them following the trot as he baited.

There was only one thing he could do—change bait. Crawdads were still good, but they were hard to come across. The ones that he found had turned a rusty brown, a sure sign of cold weather. Liver was too expensive, and anyway he had to save it for his turtle hooks. He would have to use worms and grasshoppers. Grasshoppers would be easy to catch in the horseweed patch that covered the path up the bank from the shanty-boat. Grasshoppers brought the carp, and they did not sell; but a good yellow grasshopper would also tempt a catfish.

The trotline had taken several nice catfish. John had put them in the fish box at the shantyboat. Once a week he emptied the box and took the fish to town. Some he sold for cash, and some he traded for things he needed on the boat. Small fish he turned back to the river, warning them to stop stealing his bait until they were a little bigger. He would grin as he watched the small ones swim away, happy to be free.

The leaves had begun to fall and drift on the water. The nights were colder now, and John could see winter coming everywhere he looked along the bank. The signs were on the water. The smooth surface of summer was rippled by the autumn winds. Cornstalks began to drift by the boat, and John knew that the gardens planted along the Sandy were grown and harvested. The leaves were yellowing on the willows; the maple leaves turned with the fog at night, making them look almost white against a light.

Fish had moved to deeper water, and the ones John took from the trot were coming out of the middle of the river. He caught fewer turtles, and as he worked the turtle lines he looked along the bank for signs of musk-rat and mink.

This time of year muskrat pulled the long blades of corn into their holes in the bank and their hiding places were easy to see. A hole that held a corn blade always contained a muskrat, so John knew exactly where to set his traps. The season was short, and here on the river no one could be sure how short; it all depended on the water.

But good sets were scarce after the first month. Ice and high water made trapping on the river hard except for log sets. One night the river would rise so high over a trap that it could not take a rat, and the next night the river might fall so low that the trap was left high on the bank. Traps high on the bank lost more rats than they caught. A rat trapped where he could reach deep water was quickly drowned, and he did not suffer long.

One evening as John scuddled the boat toward the creek, coming from baiting his trotline, he thought he noticed something moving on top of the snag where his last turtle line was set. He slowed the boat and moved closer to the bank. Someone was bending over the snag, trying to reach into the water. Whoever it was, he was small, perhaps only a child. John let the boat drift with the current toward the snag.

"What are you doing?" John asked severely, when he was close at hand.

He watched the small figure climb from the snag and stand on the bank staring at him.

"I seen something splashing in the water," a boyish voice said. "And I clumb to see what it was."

John watched the lad wipe his hand over the blue overalls he was wearing. The boy was a stranger to John, and he knew that he had never come to the river with the other boys that used to gather there.

"Look at me when you talk," John said. "Now . . . what was you aiming to do with the line you was holding in your hand?"

The old man studied the boy and pulled over to the snag. The boy stepped farther up the bank.

"I wasn't going to take it," he said. "Honest I wasn't. I seen the splash and looked to see what it was."

"You got no business on the river," John said, in a deep voice.

"Ma said I could come," the boy quivered.

"Bet she didn't say for you to climb out on a snag over the water. Where you live?"

"Through there," the boy said, pointing toward the willows up the bank. "I used to live over there . . ." he was pointing now at the West Virginia point . . . "but Ma said we have come here to live now."

John watched the boy's hand shake as he pointed. He knew that the child was scared.

"Well," John said, "you ought to know better than

to climb out over the water . . . and to bother something that ain't yours."

"But I wasn't going to bother nothing," the boy said, shifting his foot along the sand. "I was just going to look."

John studied him more closely. There were brown streaks of mud across his shirt where he had been leaning over the snags trying to reach the water. John could not help thinking of Jobe.

"You ought to stay away from the river," he said harshly.

"Why?" the boy asked.

"You might fall. The river don't care much for boys. It might reach up and snatch you from the limb."

The boy looked at John and laughed.

"I ain't afraid of the river," he said. "The river can't reach."

"You ought to be afraid."

"Are you afraid of the river?" the boy asked.

"Well . . . no, but then I live here, and the river knows me. And I'll bet your ma knows me—Scrapiron John?"

"That's a funny name," the boy said. "Why do they call you Scrapiron? My name is Allen."

The boy moved closer to the joeboat.

"You better be getting up the bank," John said. "Now go on . . . and don't be bothering lines."

"Can I see you raise the line before I go?"

"Reckon not. Now you go on up the bank."

"Maybe I can watch you tomorrow?"

"Run along up the bank," John said, pulling the bow of the joeboat under the snag.

He watched the boy turn and walk up the bank. Allen stopped at the edge of the willows and waved at John and smiled.

"Good-by, Mr. John," he said, as he stepped into the willows.

John pulled the boat in close and lifted the line from the water. A small carp had taken the hook. The old man slowly worked the hook out of the fish's mouth and put the carp in the water. The carp rested for a minute near the surface of the water and then swam away. John rebaited the line and started for the shantyboat.

He thought of the small boy who had stood at the edge of the willows and waved good-by. He could remember the smile. He did not know the boy, and the boy did not know him; if the boy had known him, he would have probably been afraid. But John did not think it would be long before Allen learned the name "Scrapiron," and then he would not come near the shantyboat.

The sun set behind the willows, and John watched the moon come over the water, throwing light on willow leaves that floated downstream. The river was quiet, and the night was clear. He puffed his pipe and leaned back in the chair. He wondered if the small boy would be at the snag tomorrow.

CHAPTER NINE

A WEEK PASSED, AND EVERY DAY JOHN SAW ALLEN STAND-ing on the bank above the creek. He would wave as the old man passed by in the joeboat and then run up the bank, following him as far as the snag where the trotline was tied. He never came close to the water. When John stopped at the creek to raise the turtle lines the boy stood at the edge of the willows, smiling when the shantyboat man looked at him. Yet he never came close or talked.

John found himself beginning to look for the boy on the bank as he passed the creek each day on his way to the trot. Once he even caught himself waving back from the middle of the river. Surely, he thought, the boy had mentioned his name to his parents. Yet, maybe they didn't care; maybe they understood. And then John

wondered if they *could* understand. Only one person had ever really understood him, and that was Reverend Crites. The preacher was one of the few who did not laugh or have something smart to say when he saw him.

John realized that the boy must never be allowed to come to the shantyboat. But if he stayed high on the bank . . . that would be all right. Even on the bank he was company.

The weather was colder now, and the old man had decided to leave the trot in the water another week. And then he would set his traps.

He moved along the edge of the bank on his way from the trot, hauling in the turtle lines. He knew that the turtles were moving under the mud, and he could save time by taking the lines in now. He pulled the joeboat under the snag where the last line was set. As he untied the line he noticed ripples in the water at the edge of the bank. Small pieces of mud rolling from the steep bank were making the ripples. John looked up over the snag. Allen stood at the edge of the snag looking down at him.

"Did you catch any fish today, Mr. John?" Allen asked.

John looked at the boy and smiled.

"One little one," he said. "I give him back to the river."

"Gosh," Allen said, "you mean you let him go?"

"Yep," John said, untying the turtle line.

"I wouldn't," Allen said, sitting on top of the snag. "I never have caught a fish, but if I did I wouldn't let it go; I'd take it home with me."

John laughed at the expression on the small boy's

face and said, "You'll catch a fish one of these days."

"Will I have to wait long?" Allen asked. "Maybe till my hair is white like yours, Mr. John?"

The shantyboat man cleaned the hook and laid the nib on the floor of the joeboat.

"You'll have caught a mess of them by that time," he said.

"Bet you have, ain't you, Mr. John? I'll bet you've caught enough to fill that whole boat."

"Well, I've been with the river a long time. And me and that old shantyboat down there has seen a lot of fish."

Allen looked downriver. The leaves had fallen from the willows, and from where he stood he could glimpse the shantyboat through the branches.

"Wish I lived on a shantyboat," Allen said. "Can I see yours, Mr. John?"

John looked at the boy and shoved the joeboat away from the snag.

"You better stay on the bank," he said. "Wait till you get bigger."

"Do you think I might be big enough tomorrow?" Allen asked.

The old man could not keep from laughing. "Maybe not *that* soon."

"Will you be coming tomorrow?"

"I'll be coming for a few more days," John said, picking up the oars.

"Will I be old enough then?" Allen begged, seeing the joeboat drift with the current.

"We'll see," John said, moving the oars in the water.

CHAPTER TEN

THE DAYS SEEMED TO GO FAST. JOHN WAVED AT ALLEN on the bank at the creek as he passed on the way to the trot. But he did not stop on the shore. There was only one more day left before he would quit coming to raise the trot. And then he would not come at all, except to the mouth of the creek where he would turn to set his traps. But he would be raising the traps before daylight every morning, so he could not hope to see the boy. In fact, Allen would never know that John had been to the creek at all.

Today, the old man thought, he would say good-by to the boy and then forget. He knew that he was beginning to like Allen too much. It would be better to stop now. After a few days the boy would forget him and that would be that.

John knew that Allen was watching from the bank as he took the nibs from the trot and laid them in the boat. He could see him walk from the edge of the water to the willows and then back. When the boy saw the old man looking toward the bank he would wave, and John would turn his head as if he had not seen. Allen stayed on the bank until the shantyboat man had finished taking in the trotline; and when he saw John coming closer to the bank he ran downriver to the mouth of the creek, where he stood and waited. He waved at John as the boat went by, and John waved back to him.

At dusk John took a sack from the shantyboat and walked over the plank to the shore. He turned and climbed up the bank toward an open bottom. Next to the edge of the bottom stood a large shell-barked hickory. He walked over to the hickory and lit his pipe.

"Got some more traps for you," John said, looking at the tall tree. "Have to borrow some more bark."

John stripped bark from the tree and put it in the sack. He looked toward the sky.

"Cold night," he said, as he walked toward the willows.

At the shantyboat John built a fire in the stove. He filled a large bucket with water and put it on the fire. Then he walked to the deck of the shanty and sat down. He puffed his pipe and watched the waves on the river wash against the bank. The night was clear and cold. John knew that winter was here. And it had seemed to come fast this time. Another summer, and he had not taken Scrapiron Jack.

But this was not the first such summer, and he knew that it would not be the last. Next year he could start early. He would not have to worry about his line. And there would be no need to dry the one he had. Only the nibs must be dried and he could do that tomorrow when he went to set the traps. If he put them on the deck of the shanty they would be dry by the time he came back from the creek.

At least the great fish had been in the river, he thought. And that was a good sign.

John walked into the cabin and took the bucket of boiling water off the stove. He set the bucket down to cool and took a chain of traps off the nail where they hung on the wall of the shanty. He separated the new traps from the old and laid the new traps beside the bucket.

After the water had cooled some he dipped the new traps into it one at a time. This would take the fresh smell of steel from them. A new trap was all right for muskrats, but a mink would scent the steel and not come near it. Minks were scarce, and a good mink pelt brought as much as a dozen muskrats.

John hung the traps back on the nail and lay down on the cot. Tomorrow would be a hard day. The first day was always the hardest on the trap line. He would have to carry and set all of the traps. After the first day he would only have to move traps as he saw fit.

There was a light frost on the ground when John stepped onto the bank with the sack of traps. He tied the joeboat to the log and started up the creek, stopping just inside the mouth to make a set on a log that crossed the creek. He had seen mink tracks on the log earlier, when he had set for minnows.

[68]

John knew that mink traveled the creek, and any mink that came down the river would go up this one. A mink was a curious beast. He would travel miles to the end of a creek, sometimes being gone for days; but John knew that one day he would be coming back. He would be coming back, and he would be following the same trail that he had taken up the creek—most times almost in the same tracks.

John placed the trap just below the surface of the water and dug leaves from under the mud to cover the top. Those soggy leaves would not wash away.

The old man stepped back and looked at the set and then started up the creek, staying in the middle of the stream because he did not want to leave footprints on the bank. He had lost more traps to thieves than he ever had to washouts and high water.

As John walked he looked at both banks for signs. The muskrat was not hard to catch, and he left many signs. All his years on the river and creeks had taught John these signs. He knew that the hole of the muskrat would be under water, sometimes deep and sometimes shallow. Beyond the entrance to the hole the opening curved up into the steep mud banks, out of the water. The muskrat carried corn blades and grass into the hole to make his bed in the high banks.

The tail of the muskrat gave him away in shallow water, leaving a line as he dragged it over the soft mud at the bottom of the creek bed. Most times the line could be followed right to the den of the rat.

Some holes were large and others were small. The muskrat swam shallow in the water, and to catch him you had to make him squeeze through the hole with no more than two to three inches of water over the trap. John would have to build up the large holes with mud. The muskrat was not cautious like the mink.

The slides to John were the best sets of all. A muskrat had one path that he used to come down the bank, and it was seldom that he would follow another. The slick paths were easy to find. John set his traps where the slides went into the water and covered the traps with light grass and leaves.

But, like the river, the creek had disadvantages, and shallow water was its greatest drawback. A muskrat caught in shallow water was seldom held. If the water was too shallow, John did not set but tried to find where the trail of the rat might lead to deep water. And if deep water was close he would cut a long forked willow and trim the small limbs from it, leaving them about a half-inch long. Then he would stick the straight end of the limb into the bank through the ring on the trap chain. The ring on the chain would slide over the small limbs as the rat pulled it down, but the chain could not come back to the bank. When a rat was caught in a trap the first thing he would do was pull to deep water.

The disadvantage to using the stake was that it was easy to see; anyone coming up the creek could find it. John was not the only person who recognized the signs of the muskrat and mink. And he knew that a good set was also a good place to look for someone who might be trying to find the traps. Every year he lost traps on the creek, especially since he had become deaf.

The creek was long and narrow and followed the road, some places only twenty feet away from it. Anyone coming along the road on foot or in a car could look over into the creek and see a man if he was standing up. When John saw the cars he always ducked, but he could not watch both ends of the road at once. And to him the cars made no sound as they went by. He only saw them after they had passed, and this was usually too late.

He followed the creek back, now, toward the river. He had made twenty-four good sets along the creek; he wanted to make a set or two on the river, as well. By changing sets he could work the creek with two dozen traps. And there were good signs along the river. The old snag that held his last turtle line was well located. Much of the dirt had been hollowed away from the roots by muskrat. He could put a bait set there and should be able to take a lot of muskrat before the season was over. The trap could be set high on the bank and tied to the snags low in the water.

John made the set under the snag and arranged two log sets. He cut notches in the ends of the logs and put a trap at each end. Then he tied a slice of apple to the middle of the log and let the log float out from the bank, tied so that it would not float away. Once a rat was in the water the weight of the trap kept him from climbing back to the log and he would drown instead.

Every morning as John tied the joeboat to the mouth of the creek he looked at the bank where he had first seen Allen. He missed the boy. Somehow, without his smile, John seemed to find more loneliness on the river than he had ever known before. And yet it had only been a few days now since he had seen the lad.

John still missed the other boys that used to come every day to ask him where to fish. And if he closed his eyes he could see them, poles over their shoulders, and smiles on their faces at the sight of the old man and the shantyboat. Sometimes they would sit on the back of the shantyboat and catch shiners for him to use on his trot. John could remember how they used to love to sit and listen to him tell them the story of Scrapiron Jack, and they all had believed that one day he would catch the giant catfish.

Sometimes as he sat in the chair on the deck of the shantyboat and looked up the clay path he grew angry at the river. Yet he knew that the river did not have the power to take a life. He knew that it could drown a person, but it did not have the power to choose. Sometimes he felt that he did not know anything of the river, and then again he thought he could read every wave. In spite of everything, he loved the river and was grateful to it.

One morning as he walked out of the cabin he saw that the bank was covered with snow. The willows were bent heavy trying to hold up the white drifts. John took a deep breath; the air was cold and fresh. There was no wind and the water was as smooth as if it was covered by a thin layer of ice.

John flipped the walking board over and watched the snow fall to the water. Then he stepped into the joeboat and paddled upriver to the creek, checking his river sets on the way.

The creek banks were smooth and even, and John knew that it had snowed earlier in the morning. If it had snowed during the night there would have been tracks of some kind on the snow. There were, of course, bird tracks under the trees, but birds wre so plentiful that their tracks would always cover the snow as quickly as it fell. The snow had been light, and the night had not been too cold. There must have been lots of traveling on the creek, John thought.

He passed the mink set near the mouth of the brook and saw that it had not been touched. Then, following the stream he started upcreek.

Out of the next twenty traps three had been sprung; one held the foot of a muskrat, and four had been stolen. And all four of the missing traps had been the ones that John had fixed with the willow forks. He pushed the snow off the ground above the places where the traps were missing, and he saw footprints in the mud. John knew that someone had seen him making the sets. He knew that it was not a trapper; at least not a good trapper, or he would have gotten the others. It could have been a hunter or someone that had seen him from the road.

John took his time and tried to hide the traps better, and he thought that he would check them on his way back down the creek.

This side of the last trap John stopped. He could see something splashing in the water. Whatever it was it seemed to be caught in the trap. John knew that he had baited the last trap with corn, and he supposed that it was holding a rat. He splashed up the creek toward the trap, fearing that the rat might pull loose.

He stopped in front of the trap. Inside was a small wild duck which had been trying to get the corn and had got caught in the trap. He bent down and the duck flapped one of its wings, splashing cold water into his face. John put one hand around the wings of the duck and pried open the jaws of the trap with the other. He looked at the duck's leg and knew it was broken. The left wing was also broken, and many of the tip feathers had been pulled out.

"Didn't set the trap for you, little fellow," John said sadly, holding the duck in his arms. "You got a bad-looking leg."

He stood for a minute in the creek, wondering what to do with the duck. If he turned it loose on the creek it would starve to death because it could not search for food. Or if it did not starve it would either freeze or be eaten by a dog or some other animal. He looked at the leg and wing, and he knew that they were painful. Putting the duck in his sack, he started down the creek.

At the shantyboat John sat down by the fire and started whittling splints for the duck's leg. He figured that the wing would straighten itself. He took the duck out of the sack and set it beside the stove to get warm. The duck did not move; it seemed to have little fear of him. From time to time he walked over to it to measure the splints along its leg. After the duck was well, he decided, he would turn it loose.

"Now . . . how's that?" John said, as he fastened the

splints on the duck. "You might have to limp for a while, but old John will see to it that you don't starve. You can live right here on the shantyboat with me till you get well enough to fly. Reckon that's the best I can do to make up for catching you in the trap."

Next morning John was up at the break of day. He shelled some corn for the duck and paddled the joeboat to the creek. At its mouth he saw some footprints on the side of the bank. The footprints were small, like those of a boy. John followed the tracks in the snow with his eyes until they disappeared into the willows. He wondered if the tracks could be Allen's. They looked as if they had been made the day before, sometime before dark.

All the way up the creek John thought of the track and the boy. Two more traps were missing from the line, and he had two good rats. He started down the creek. From now on he would have to run the traps twice a day. In the morning he could hide the traps beside the sets, and just before dark he would have to come back and set.

A light snow was falling as John opened the door to the cabin.

"Well, Limpy," he said, picking up some wood and putting it on the fire, "bad weather out there, it's going to be. Ought to be glad you're in the warm. Are you hungry?"

He took an ear of corn from the string on the wall and shelled off a few grains. He held the corn a few feet from the duck and watched it limp over to his hand. John rubbed his hand over its feathers as it ate the corn.

"You're a funny duck, Limpy," he said, wondering why it wasn't afraid of him.

After the duck had eaten, John took his knife and trimmed the broken feathers on its wing. The duck sat in John's lap pecking at his hand with its flat bill.

CHAPTER ELEVEN

IN TWO DAYS THE SNOW HAD MELTED FROM THE BANKS. And during that time John had caught four rats and lost three more traps. He was traveling the line twice a day, and still the traps were being stolen. He knew that he could not afford to lose traps, especially this fast. He was hiding them as best he knew how, and he had turned down good rat sets because they were too much out in the open.

On the creek was where John missed his hearing the most. He did not need it so badly when he was fishing on the river. But now if he had his hearing he would not be losing so many traps. And he would stand a chance of catching the thief, whoever he was.

John noticed the dark clouds in the sky as he walked

down the creek. They were rain clouds, and he knew that if the rains came the creek would wash out. The ground was already heavy with water. The rain would bring a lot of work, too. All of the traps would have to be carried back to the shantyboat and reset after the creek settled. If they were left in the water during the rain they would be washed down the creek and buried in brush piles and mud. The banks would cave in on many, and all of them would not be dug out.

At the mouth of the creek John noticed a movement in the willows. He moved close to the bank, thinking it might be someone looking for traps. The bank was steep, and he could not see above it. John waited, wishing he could hear. He waited and could see nothing, and then he stepped out into the creek and looked toward the bank.

Allen stood at the edge of the willows watching the joeboat tied at the mouth of the creek. He turned quickly and saw John, and then he walked to the edge of the bank smiling.

"I seen your boat, Mr. John," he said. "I been waiting. I seen you go up the creek yesterday, and I came to the river to wait. But it got dark and I couldn't stay."

John stepped out of the water toward the boat, keeping his eye on the boy.

"Why do you go up the creek every day, Mr. John?" Allen asked.

"How do you know I go up every day?"

"I see you," Allen said. "I seen you every day. I can see you from the house. Yesterday I seen you and I said, 'Look, Ma, there goes Mr. John.' Ma looked out the

[79]

window, and she said that you was setting traps. She said that Pa used to set traps when he was living."

John let go of the rope to the boat and lighted his pipe.

"Why didn't you ever come to the mouth of the creek when you seen me going up?" John said.

"I did," Allen said. "But you always stay up the creek too long, Mr. John. I'm not allowed on the river after dark."

John scratched a match across the board on the boat and lighted his pipe again. Then he looked at Allen and smiled.

"Tell you what," John said; "maybe I'll wait for you tomorrow. I might even let you go with me, providing your ma don't care."

"All the way up the creek?" Allen asked.

"Yep," John said. "I'll have you back before dark."

"Ma won't care," Allen said. "I know she won't."

"You ask just the same," John said. "I'll wait a while here at the mouth, and if you don't come I'll know you can't go."

John looked at the boy's face, and it almost made tears come to his eyes. But he knew that he himself was even happier than the boy. He waved at Allen and shoved the boat from the bank.

John tied the joeboat and walked into the cabin.

"Going to have company, maybe, tomorrow, Limpy," he said, shelling some corn and holding it out to the duck.

Limpy waddled across the floor and started scooping

up the grains of corn. While the duck ate John looked at the broken leg. The splints were ready to come off. John held the duck and untied the splints. He could see that the duck's leg was crooked, and he knew that it would always be crooked. Limpy would always walk crippled. The wing had healed, but it would be of little use in flying. John looked at the two beady eyes that moved back and forth from one grain of corn to the other.

"I'm sorry about the leg and wing, Limpy," John said. "Ain't much more I can do. Offer you a home with me here on the boat if you want to stay. You won't be able to fly with the others, and it gets mighty lonesome by yourself."

The duck ate the last of the corn and limped over to the water that John had set down in a pan. The wounded creature tried to stand on one leg as it drank, but fell. The old man got on his knees and held it close to the pan.

"You'll get used to the leg, Limpy," he said. "I reckon there is some things that birds, just like people, has got to get used to."

John lay down on the cot. There was a lot on his mind, and he could not sleep. He watched the light from the fire in the stove flicker across the back of the duck, lying close by with its head hid under its wing. He was sorry for the crippled duck, but there was nothing he could do for it.

John thought of Allen. The boy's ma had not said anything about John when she had seen him going up the creek. If Allen was at the creek tomorrow evening he would know that it was all right to take the lad up the creek. He wondered if the woman would be watching from the window as he passed with the boy and if she would change her mind and call Allen from the creek. John planned to watch the boy around the water and to keep him safe on the high bank.

At daylight John was up. He waded through the cold water of the creek checking each trap. He took one large rat from the next to the last trap, but he knew that the hide was almost useless; it had been torn so badly by other rats that it was hardly worth skinning. John could not understand why one rat would attack another in a trap. But he knew that they would. He knew that they would slash the hide with their powerful teeth until the trapped rat was dead.

John scuddled the boat toward the shantyboat, glad that the morning raise was over. As he neared the shanty he saw that the door to the cabin must have been left open; Limpy was standing out on the small deck looking down into the water.

John took the oars from the locks and let the boat drift alongside the shanty, trying not to scare the duck. He eased the rope around the tiepost, talking to Limpy in a low voice, and stepped onto the boat. The duck turned his head from side to side and then scuttled over to John. John noticed that it had begun to use its crippled leg more. He rubbed the duck's feathers and called to it as he walked toward the cabin. And the duck followed.

John smiled and shelled some corn. Limpy had become used to following him everywhere he walked around the cabin, and this was odd for a wild duck. Not many ever became pets.

CHAPTER TWELVE

A LIGHT SNOW FELL AS JOHN STEPPED OUT OF THE CABIN and walked toward the joeboat. As he rowed upriver the wind blew the snow into his face. He could see Allen standing on the bank above the creek, looking downriver. John pulled the boat up to the bank and tied in above the log. He stuck an apple and ear of corn in his pocket to use for bait. Then he crossed the creek and joined Allen.

"Going to let you help me with the sets."

"You mean get in the water like you do, Mr. John?" the lad said, looking at the boots the old man was wearing.

John laughed and glanced at the boy's small leather shoes.

"You can help set from the bank," he said. "But it will take a keen eye."

Allen did not answer. He looked at John and listened.

"Another thing, Old John can't hear too good," John said, "and someone's been stealing my traps. I was thinking maybe you could be my ears."

Allen looked at John.

"Do you reckon I could?" he said frowning.

"You get a pocketful of small rocks," John told him, in a low voice, "and you sneak along the bank. When you see a car or someone coming you hit me with a rock and I'll know to duck so I can't be seen. When things is clear you hit me with a rock again. Do you reckon you could do that?"

"Yes, sir," the boy said, "if I can just get me a pocketful of rocks."

"Look for the rocks on the way," the old man said. "And keep a keen eye toward the road."

John moved around the mink set and started upcreek. He walked slowly so that the boy could keep pace.

A short way up the creek he felt a rock hit his shoulder, and he ducked to the bank. He turned around slowly and watched the small boy hunker into a grove of willows. John smiled and looked upcreek. Then pretty soon another rock hit his back and he straightened up.

During the week not a trap was lost. Allen had carried his rocks to the mouth of the creek and had covered them with sand so that they could not be seen. John knew that the boy watched the rocks closer during the day than he himself watched his traps.

When they came from the creek the old man took time to sit and talk to Allen. He began to tell him many things about the river. And of course he told him about Scrapiron Jack. When he mentioned Limpy, Allen wanted to go to the boat to see him right away. John promised him that he could come to the shantyboat when the snows melted.

And with the melting of the snows John moved his traps from the creek and used them on river sets. Allen came every day to watch from the bank. During the day he would sit there and watch the lines that held the logs out in the water. John had given one of the sets to the boy, telling him that if it caught a rat he would use the money from the hide to buy a line so that Allen could fish when the summer came. John laughed when the boy spoke of catching Scrapiron Jack.

And so the loneliness of the river seemed to disappear and the days passed fast. John took the traps and put them back on the nail inside the cabin. He began to spend more time on the shantyboat working on his fishing line and traps.

Limpy would not leave the boat. He came out on the deck as he pleased and stood in the warm sun while John worked. Only one time had the duck gone to warm water. A flock of wild ducks flew over, circling low to the boat. Limpy had looked over the side. He swam a short piece and then turned and came back to the shantyboat and John lifted him from the water.

Limpy scuttled over to the chair where John was sitting and pecked at the loose line dangling on the deck.

"Won't be long, Limpy," the old man said, tying a

[88]

knot in the end of the line he was holding. "We got to be getting ready for Scrapiron Jack."

John's attention was centered now on the long coil of line. It would not be long until the line would be stretched, he thought, glancing at the sky.

"Sun's getting low," he commented. "Told Allen I'd be at the creek to set the minnow traps."

John gathered the minnow traps from the cabin and placed them in the floor of the joeboat. Limpy followed John as he walked to the cabin for the oars.

"Might let you meet him tomorrow, Limpy," John said, shoving the joeboat away from the shanty. "You won't be scared of Allen."

John rowed the boat to the creek, where the lad stood on the bank.

"Did you get my line fixed, Mr. John?" he asked as the old man pulled the joeboat up into the mouth of the creek.

"Yep," John said, smiling at the boy. "And tomorrow you can see it."

"You mean I can go to the boat with you?" Allen said.

"Yep," John said, "you can meet Limpy, and I might let you fish a spell from the back of the boat."

John watched the boy dance up and down in the sand. John saw his feet were bare now. Summer was here already, he thought. It wouldn't be long until the rains came. And with the rains would come Scrapiron Jack.

John baited the traps with bread crumbs and lowered them into the water. He explained to Allen how the minnows swam inside the trap and then could not find their way out again. Allen laughed.

[89]

"Minnows sure are dumb, ain't they, Mr. John?" he said.

The old man laughed and stepped up on the bank to sit a while and talk.

"Do you think that Limpy will like me, Mr. John?" Allen said, digging his feet into the sand.

"I reckon," John said. "May be scared a little at first. He ain't ever had company before."

"I'll bet he gets lonesome on the boat."

John blew puffs of smoke into the wind and looked across the water. "Not too much he don't," he said.

"But don't he miss the other ducks?"

"He'll get to see them again next year when the weather is cold."

"Will he go away with them when they fly over the boat next year, Mr. John?" Allen asked.

John rose to his feet and stretched. He knocked the ashes from his pipe.

"I don't expect so," he said, thinking of the crippled wing and foot of the duck. "But don't you worry about Limpy; he's happy on the boat."

CHAPTER THIRTEEN

JOHN DROPPED THE ROCK SINKER INTO THE WATER ON THE West Virginia side and watched the line play out. Then he started to the snag where he had tied the joeboat. Allen had been on the bank most of the morning, and John had waved at him several times.

John pulled the joeboat into the mouth of the creek beside the minnow traps. He raised the traps and watched Allen's eyes widen as he looked at the minnows flipping inside.

Allen got in the boat, and John motioned for him to sit in the back seat so that the joeboat would be easier to handle on the way to the snag.

John pulled the line from the water, and Allen handed him the white minnows as he passed the hooks. John used a few crawdads toward the middle of the trot. While he baited he told Allen about the big fish that would come out of the Ohio.

When they reached the shantyboat John lifted the boy from the joeboat. Limpy was out on the deck. He looked at Allen and waddled to John. John picked him up, rubbing his feathers. He let Allen pet him. And when he set the duck down it was no longer afraid.

While Allen fished from the back of the shantyboat John sat in the chair and made his turtle lines. He was only replacing the hooks. The line had dried during the winter. Hooks could not be left on line that was long out of the water; they would rust and cut through the line.

After a while the young fisherman spoke up. "You know, Mr. John," he said, "I don't believe this line is big enough to hold Scrapiron Jack."

John looked at the short line, willow pole, and bobber. He laughed and slid a hook through the turtle line.

"Might be I'll have to make you a bigger one in a day or so," he said, knowing that Allen was still thinking of the large trotline.

Then suddenly the bobber went under the water, and the boy jerked.

"Get him, Allen!" John said.

Pretty soon the bobber hit the deck, and a river shiner flipped off the hook and flopped up and down on the boards. Limpy ruffled his feathers and looked at the minnow. Then he waddled over to John.

When the sun set the old man took the boy back to the creek.

Allen began to come to the boat by himself now. The hot sun had made the shallow water of the creek warm enough to wade. Every day Allen sat and fished off the back of the shanty and listened to the stories of the river. He had begged John to let him take Limpy along when they went to raise the trotline, and John had allowed the boy to sit in the back of the joeboat with Limpy on his lap. But now the duck was spoiled. Every time John walked out on the deck Limpy started for the boat.

New leaves had come to the willows, and John thought they looked like green walls on both sides of the river.

He sat on the deck of the shantyboat and studied the dark clouds in the sky. The rains would soon be coming to the river, and with the rains would come the fish that he hoped to catch. The new trotline reached clear across the river, and John knew that anything swimming up the stream would have to see the line. And he did not think that Scrapiron Jack would pass the soft creek minnows and crawdads. The old man could count on plenty of crawdads. Every day Allen brought him more that he caught under the rocks in the creek bed on his way to the boat.

Then the sun moved behind the dark clouds. These clouds had been building up for almost a week. The wind had gotten strong along the river, and John thought that the rain might come a little early this year. Wind made the trotline hard to bait. It was almost impossible to hold the boat steady in the wind and keep it from drifting back and forth under the trot. So Allen often sat in the stern and scuddled with a paddle to keep the boat straight while the old man baited the hooks.

Allen was late today, John thought. He knew that he had waited as long as he should. So he untied the joe-boat and rowed toward the creek. Allen wasn't on the bank. The old man went on to the trot, baited the line, and rowed back to the shantyboat.

Perhaps the boy had something to do at the house, John thought, as he whittled out a willow pole for the larger line he had promised to make. The line would hold two hooks and a sinker, and Allen would be able to fish on the bottom where he could catch larger fish. John knew the lad would be mighty excited when he saw the new line.

After this John laid the pole on the deck and walked to the bank. He took his knife and cut several willow limbs and walked back to the boat. He trimmed the ends of the willow poles and lowered them over the side into the water. He thought that he would be making another rocker this year.

A week passed, and still Allen did not come. John was worried. Not really worried about anything happening to the boy, but perhaps his ma had stopped him from coming to the river. Maybe she had told Allen to stay away from the shantyboat. Maybe she had heard of "Scrapiron" and had believed some of the things she had heard in town—maybe some of the awful things they said about Jobe's drowning.

Of course, she knew the boy had been coming to the boat. Allen had said so many times, and John did not think Allen would lie to him. John wondered if the boy's mother would understand the love he had for the boy, and the loneliness he now felt.

He knew that he should not wait so long at the shanty during the day. It was time to think of Scrapiron Jack. And if he was to catch the big catfish his mind must be crystal clear.

John got up from the chair where he had been sitting on the deck and walked into the cabin. He came out carrying the box of crawdads. Limpy followed him to the joeboat, and John took him back to the cabin and closed the door. He knew that it was late in the day to bait the line. But at least he could check the bait before dark. Night was the time when the catfish ran the river. During the day at this time of year it was mostly carp and gars, and both of them were bait stealers.

John untied the joeboat and paddled upriver. He moved slowly past the creek, looking along the edge of the willows. The willows were getting so heavy with leaves that he could not see far into them.

He noticed signs of the river. The water was rippled, and there was a wind in the trees. Rain was sure to come. He looked at the dark clouds which made the shadows of the willows disappear from the river.

A streak of lightning broke above the tops of the willows, and John knew he would have to hurry if he was to bait before dark. The rain would surely come tonight, but he did not think that it would be a hard rain. And he was glad, after all, that he had waited until late to check the trot. A rain along the river seemed to make the fish bite, and he knew that tonight his line would be ready.

John pulled the boat alongside the snag and tied it up while he set the bait within easy reach in the bow. He knew that the wind would make baiting hard, and it was almost dark.

He leaned over the front of the boat, stuck his hand in the water, and pulled up the line. Then he held it to see if he could feel anything on it. But he felt only the current of the water.

Steadying the boat with the trotline, he moved out into the river, stopping at each nib to bait. When he came to the end of the line he pulled the sinker from the water and rowed upriver. He did not drop the line as close as usual to the West Virginia side. If the rains should come harder than he thought, the Big Sandy might run out, carrying brush and snags with it. The river could become so swift in a single night that he could not row against the current. With slack in the line the trot could drift with a strong current, and the pressure would not be as great as it would be on a line tied solid.

As John dropped the sinker he looked again at the clouds. There was no sign of a heavy rain. The clouds were moving upriver, bearing toward the Kentucky side. John knew that the rain would fall somewhere, but he did not think it would be close enough to the Sandy to cause the river to swell. The ground was dry and could take most of the water.

A light rain was coming down as John pulled the joe-boat up to the shanty. He tied the boat and carried the crawdads into the cabin.

And now darkness came early to the river, and John sat beside the oil lamp and thought of Scrapiron Jack.

He fumbled a willow branch in his hand, twisting it in a circle to form part of the back of the rocking chair he was making. He could feel the shanty swaying with the water, and he knew that the river was getting rough. He dropped the willow branch and walked to the door of the cabin. Limpy ambled out onto the deck. John held his hand out into the rain.

"Come on, Limpy," he said, "you're liable to get caught in a storm."

CHAPTER FOURTEEN

A LIGHT FOG HUNG OVER THE WATER AS JOHN STEPPED
out of the cabin. The rain had become a light drizzle.
He straightened the rim of his hat to block the rain from
his eyes and started upriver toward the snag.

He was almost on the snag before he could see it
through the fog. He lighted his pipe and held the line.
He could feel the steady jerk, and he knew that about
halfway out the line was holding a fish. John thought
it would be best to raise the line and take the fish and
bait on the way back.

At the middle of the line John took a fine blue cat
off the trot. Then he felt the line again. He knew that
at the snag he could feel as far as the first jerk and not
beyond. The line could easily be holding another fish.
He felt a second jerk.

The last hook on the trot held another catfish, this time a channel cat that John judged to weigh about five pounds. He put the cat beside the first one on the floor of the boat and turned to bait the line, moving slowly toward the Kentucky side.

The fog had lifted by the time John finished baiting the line, but the light rain still fell. He scuddled the boat back to the shanty, looking at the clouds. They were still dark, but they were also still moving upriver. This was not a sign of rain.

But John knew that many times the river gave no signs. A rain could come fast, without warning, and in a moment the river could be running swift.

Most of the day John sat in the cabin. The rain had become harder, and John could feel the movement of the current against the shantyboat. Once he walked to the back of the boat to pull loose a drift pile that had caught. Then he sat in the chair and whittled on a large driftwood board. He planned to make the rockers for the chair out of this. Allen would not come today, he felt sure; the weather was too bad. Yet John admitted to himself that there had been several good fishing days, and still the boy had not come. Maybe he would never come. John shook his head and watched Limpy peck at the end of the board he was whittling.

Before dark the old man went to the trot to bait. If the rain came slow this would be a good night for the fish. He took pains to bait, working the soft crawdads on the hooks to stand against a current. The creek had been running out when he had passed, but it did not take a heavy rain to cause this.

By the time he got back to the shanty John was soaked. He bailed some of the water from the joeboat and walked into the cabin. He had not liked the looks of the clouds. They had stopped moving, and the wind was high in the willows.

By dark the rain was harder. John could feel the beat of the rain against the side of the cabin. The wind was hard enough to slam shut the door to the cabin, and lightning flashed over the river. And, although John could not hear, he knew that thunder followed lightning. He did not like the signs, or the raise that was in the river. He thought of his trotline.

John took his lantern from the wall and walked to the door. He looked out into the rain. He lighted his pipe and sat down on the cot to wait for daylight.

Daylight began to break, but the rain did not stop. John waited to see if it was going to slack, and then he walked out to the joeboat with the lantern. Small piles of brush were floating past the boat, and he knew that the river was swift enough to wash brush into his trotline. He had misjudged the river and he became angry at himself. All of his life on the river, he told himself, and he had misjudged the signs. And this time he stood to lose the best line he had ever owned.

There was one thing he could do: take the line from the river. John knew that once he was in the boat he could judge the swiftness of the water. It must be swift; he could see that from the shanty. It looked almost too swift to row against. Then, too, he was not young and could not stand long with the oars against a swift current.

He brought the oars from the cabin and stepped into the joeboat. He bailed some water from the boat before he untied and moved away from the shanty.

The first pull on the oars told John that the river was swift enough to tangle a line. He knew that he must keep a steady stroke on the oars or he would lose ground.

He moved out in the river to avoid the swift current caused by the creek and then turned in toward the bank after he was past.

When he reached the snag he tied in. The hard row up the river had made his arms and back cramp. The rain had made seeing hard, and he wiped the water from his face and tried to light his pipe. The clouds were still black. They had begun to move upriver. But it was too late now, John thought, as he watched piles of brush float by. The river was choppy and swift. The clouds he had watched go upriver had turned and emptied into the Sandy. The river would become swifter now.

He moved slowly to the bow of the boat and felt in the water for the trot. The water was shoulder-high on the snag. He felt the line and pulled it up. Then he held the line in his hand and felt the strong current pulling the line tight.

For the first time in his life John was glad that he did not have to worry about taking fish from the line. He knew that he would have to hurry if he was to get the trot out of the river.

Slowly he started out into the water. At the first hook he stopped. He thought that he felt a pull on the line. And it did not feel like the pull of a fish. It was not a jerk . . . just a slow, steady pull, more like the pull of

a log. John shook his head at the thought of having to shake a water-soaked log from the trot in the swift water.

John knew that he would not be able to raise the trot with a log on it. The water was too swift, and it was still not light enough to see. Heavy brush piles could easily capsize the boat. The hard pull carried the trotline downriver.

John fastened the line to the back of the boat and rowed downstream, trying to pull the line loose from the other side of the log which he thought must be doubled in the nibs. But the line drifted fast, and John could not hold with the current. The trotline was getting closer to shore, and John knew that once it was drawn tight against the snag there was a good chance of its breaking.

There was one way that he might save the line: cut it at the snag, tie it to the joeboat, and drift with the trot to the shanty. There he could tie, and he would stand a better chance of shaking the log. The banks would be clearer, and if the line drifted close to the shore it would not be apt to snag on willows.

John looked at the sky, wishing that the black clouds would break so that more light could come through. Making a new trot was hard, and getting together money for another one would be even harder.

He reached into his pocket for his knife and, bending over the end of the boat, caught the trot in his hand. He stopped. There had been a jerk on the line; a hard jerk. The line began to move upriver. John took a deep breath. He knew that a log could not move against the current, and no fish could pull against this current except one . . . Scrapiron Jack.

Cold chills ran over the old man at the thought of having the great fish hooked on the trot. He felt the steady pull on the line and blinked his eyes, trying to push out some of the rain. John knew he must think. There was no time to worry about the swift water and the bad time it was to have hooked the catfish. He knew that everything depended on his keeping a clear mind. In seconds the fish might be gone. And then he would lose not only the fish, but the trotline, too. John thought of the years he had waited for this chance. But he had not figured that when the time came he would have to match his wits against the river and the fish both at once.

He knew he could not pull the great catfish into the boat with or without the current. One thing, however, stood in his favor; the catfish was hooked good. Otherwise he would not have stayed on the line this long. With luck, the fish could be tangled in the trotline.

John pulled back toward the snag. If he could take the log down the river to the shanty, maybe he could take the fish, too. He chose a strong cord and looped it around and around the trot and tied. The other end of the cord he fastened to the joeboat. Then, cutting the trotline near the snag, he tied the end of it to the joeboat. The boat began to drift with the current. John scooted to the stern and guided with an oar toward the shanty. Whatever happened he would go with the fish.

He could no longer feel the rain beating against his soaked clothing. Once he lifted the oar from the water long enough to bail water from the boat. The pressure on the line was not too heavy now.

The shantyboat came into sight, and John breathed

more deeply as he noticed the slack in the trot. He put the oars in the locks and rowed toward the shanty. With luck, there would be enough slack to get there without putting pressure on the fish.

John pulled the joeboat in to the shanty and quickly tied the trotline to the tiepost. Then he stepped out of the joeboat and watched the slack disappear from the line.

He went into the cabin door and lighted his pipe. The real job was yet to come, but he smiled at the thought of having Scrapiron Jack so close. If he could get the fish to the boat he knew that he would have beaten him—beaten a fish that had made a fool of all the rivermen. Caught at last by an old man that had taken the name of the fish because of his long years of searching the river. The people in town would not laugh any more, John thought. It would no longer be the old man and the shantyboat they joked about.

But he reminded himself that the fish was not caught yet; and, knocking the ashes from his pipe, he walked back into the rain. He sat down on the deck, bracing his feet against the tiepost, and began to pull in the slack from the line. He knew that once the pressure was on the fish it would fight for its life.

The line began to pile higher beside John, and he became more nervous. The thought of the fish began to scare him. He stopped to rest and think. John felt the line spin through his hand, cutting into the flesh. He felt the burn of the cord. The line was jerked from his hand, but the tiepost held solid. The tight line moved up and down the river, and John knew there was nothing to do but wait.

Daylight broke, but it was a misty light. The rain had slacked to a drizzle. John saw small streaks of lightning break above the tall hills beyond the river. The heavy clouds were moving upriver.

Slack came to the trotline, and John began to pull in. This time he wound the slack around the tiepost. His hands burned and bled from the rope cuts. His legs cramped, and his arms were tired. John knew from the slack that the fish was moving slowly toward the shantyboat. If Scrapiron Jack did not decide to turn, John knew that this would be a break he had not counted on. But still the fight was far from over.

How long it would take to wear the great fish down he did not know. Maybe Scrapiron Jack could outlast him. John knew that both of them were old. But a fish lost power slowly with age.

John felt his own muscles tiring. His legs cramped worse than ever. He felt weak, weaker than he had ever been before. But he knew that he would never give up; he would die holding to the trotline.

He wanted his pipe; yet he knew that the slack must be taken from the line, and the fish was still moving toward the boat. If Allen were here, he thought, he would fetch the pipe and talk while John pulled in the slack. But there was no time for talking now; and there was no time to think of Allen. John knew that he must think only of the catfish.

The rain stopped, and it became lighter. John could see the water. He judged the swiftness of the water. It was a blackish-green. From the rope on the tiepost he judged how much line was left in the water. Scrapiron Jack was closer than he had figured. And the slack was still coming. His tired muscles ached as he wound in the line.

The slack stopped, and the line became tight. John knew that the fish was fighting for its life. Several times he could see swirls on the surface of the water, but he could not see the fish itself. John began to wonder if the line would hold.

More slack came in the line, and John wound it around the post. As he moved his tired arms he wondered if the fish would ever give up. John was tired. He was tired of fighting the fish. He was tired of fighting the current. Yet he knew that there couldn't be much line left in the river.

A break came to the surface of the water and close to the boat. And John saw a large blue tail. The great catfish surfaced and rolled with the line. He was wrapped in the trot and he was held fast there.

Slowly the fish drifted to the shanty, resting a few inches below the surface of the water. John wiped his eyes with the sleeve of his wet shirt and looked down at the fish.

"Scrapiron," he said, "I got you to the boat. It looks like old John has beaten you at last. What do you say to that?"

John laughed and measured the size of the fish with his eyes. He was almost as big as the joeboat. John watched the large mouth of the catfish open and close.

The long, black whiskers on the sides of the mouth swayed with the current.

"It could be that you're trying to talk," John said, watching the mouth of the catfish. "Could be that you're trying to ask old John to let you go, couldn't it? But I ain't."

John looked at the fish. The two black eyes set deep on the sides of the broad head. The fish was bleeding from the mouth and body. Several hooks had him caught in the side.

John watched the small circles of blood come to the surface of the water and drift away with the current.

"I ain't trying to punish you, Scrapiron," John said, looking at the blood. "But there ain't no way I can ease the pain. If I loosened the hooks from you, you would zip away into the river and be gone, maybe forever. I am old and might not live to hook you again."

John lighted his pipe and blew smoke into the air.

"I knew you was my friend, River," John said. "You have given me the greatest thing you had the power to give when you give me this fish."

John looked back at Scrapiron Jack. He still did not like to see the blood. He knew that this old cat was a great fish. But here he is, John thought, floating on top of the water, maybe bleeding to death. Still, it was only natural that the fish should bleed. The fish was old, but so was John.

Yet Scrapiron Jack did not show his age. Only his size told the years that he had lived on the river.

"What is the matter with you, John?" the old man asked himself. "It is only a fish. The river knows that you have taken a lot of fish and seen them bleed before."

Yet John understood that this was not just a fish; this was Scrapiron Jack.

"What are you looking at?" John said, glaring down at the catfish. "I'm going to take you. I'm going to the bank and cut me a willow fork to run through your gills, and then I'm going to pull you to the bank and take you uptown."

John walked to the bank. He looked along the path for a good-sized fork he could use for the fish's gills. Rain had knocked the horseweeds along the path, and wind blew water from the trees. John squinted his eyes and looked up the path. Someone was coming.

John stood in the path and waited. The man in front was Sheriff Lemesters.

"What brings you to the river, Sheriff?" John said, smiling.

He watched Sheriff Lemesters staring at the wet clothes John was wearing. The hat shaded John's eyes, and he shoved it back.

"Sorry, John," Sheriff Lemesters said, "but I got a warrant for you. Reckon I've come to take you uptown."

John stood in the path and looked at Sheriff Lemesters. The sheriff had always been his friend. But he did not like the look on the man's face.

"You'll have to come," Sheriff Lemesters said.

John was tired and he could not think clearly. He felt weak.

"But I can't go now, Sheriff," he said, pointing toward the tiepost on the shantyboat. "I got . . . ."

"I don't like this," Sheriff Lemesters said. "Don't make it harder."

John looked at the boat. He could see the rope on the tiepost. He turned and started up the bank.

CHAPTER FIFTEEN

AT THE SHERIFF'S OFFICE LEMESTERS WALKED INTO THE small cell with John and explained to him about the charges of the warrant.

John listened as Sheriff Lemesters told him that Allen was missing. The boy had disappeared a week ago. And he had last been seen going down the path leading to the shantyboat. The boy's mother had warned Allen about going to the shanty after she and her son had quarreled. Apparently the boy had taken John's side against hers. Then some friends had told her about Jobe, and she had become frightened. She had whipped the boy when he had praised John, and then he had disappeared. And now she had sworn out this warrant.

John wiped his eyes as he listened. He tried to answer

the questions that were asked, but all he could say was that the boy came to the boat and spent a lot of time with him. He explained that he had not seen Allen for several days. The thought that he would hurt the boy brought tears to his eyes. He tried to tell Sheriff Lemesters that he had to get back to the shanty, but Sheriff Lemesters said that there was nothing he could do.

John knew that no one would understand his love for the boy. They could not understand that he, too, was worried. He was afraid that Allen had fallen into the river on the way to the shantyboat. The river was swift.

John sat alone in the cell. He looked out the small window at the side of the cell. Dark clouds were in the sky. The clouds looked heavy, and John knew that a bad storm was coming. It was beginning to get dark, and the day had just begun. The rains would come— maybe enough to wash the shantyboat away. The river was heavy with water now. He thought of the great catfish, helpless on the end of the trot, tied to the boat. Maybe it was a bad omen, he thought. Maybe it was wrong to take the fish from the river. To be free now seemed to have more meaning. And it did not matter any more whether the people in town saw the fish or not. What they thought about him did not matter, either. Tears filled his eyes. He was tired . . . so tired that he didn't care about anything.

The rains came. They came late in the day. John sat on the small cot and watched the rain beat against the window. Every time he closed his eyes he could see the river tearing loose chunks of the mud from the high banks. He could see the great catfish fighting to keep the hooks from cutting deeper in its side as it moved with the swift current. They were hooks that John had put there. He could see Allen being rolled with the current toward the Ohio. John shook his head and wiped the tears from his face.

The night passed slowly, and with daylight came more rain. John looked at the window, waiting for more questions to be asked.

Sheriff Lemesters opened the cell and walked in.

"Someone to see you, John," he said.

John looked toward the door. Reverend Crites walked over to the cot and sat down.

"Came as quick as I could, John," he said.

"I don't know anything about the boy, Reverent. I wouldn't hurt him. Why don't they understand?"

"I know," Reverend Crites said. "Everything is going to be all right, John."

The old man looked toward the window. The rain beat against the glass.

"I asked them to look after my boat," he said. "The rain is heavy. The boat ain't much, but it's my home. The river is swift."

"I'll see about the boat, John," Reverend Crites said. "I'll see about it myself. And don't you worry; I'll do everything I can to get you released."

The preacher got up from the cot.

"Reverent," John said, as the clergyman started for the door.

Reverend Crites turned and looked at the grief-stricken old man.

"Yes, John," he said, walking toward the cot.

"I've caught the fish," John said. "Old Scrapiron Jack."

"You really mean it?" Reverend Crites was smiling. "After all these years?"

"And you know, Reverent, there's a funny thing about that fish."

"What's that, John?"

"Well, now that I got him I don't even know that I want him."

"How is that, John?" Reverend Crites said, a surprised look on his face.

"Well, old Scrapiron is old. That fish has been with the river a long time."

"And so have you, John."

"I know," the old man said, "but I ain't ever been penned up before until now. And I been figuring that the trotline is to Scrapiron Jack about what this cell is to me. Maybe it ain't right for me to take the fish. What do you think, Reverent?"

The preacher moved his hand over his eyes.

"Use the signs of the river, John," he said. "Just remember that every sign has been put there by God."

Reverend Crites walked out the door.

"I'll see about the boat," he said. "Don't you worry."

CHAPTER SIXTEEN

DURING THE NIGHT THE RAIN STOPPED. THE SKY WAS clear when John awoke. He looked out the window. He knew that there had been enough rain to wash the shanty from the willow. But it no longer seemed to matter. The fish did not matter either. John only knew that he was tired.

He sat on the cot, waiting to tell people over and over again that he did not know where the boy was.

"John," Sheriff Lemesters said, walking into the cell, "you're free to go."

John looked up at the Sheriff.

"The boy's come home," the man went on. "Funny thing . . . he came back thinking that you might be needing help with the boat during the storm. Told me to ask you about Limpy."

John walked to the door.

Sheriff Lemesters put his arm on the old man's shoulder.

"I want you to know, John," he said, "I was just doing what I had to do. You know that."

"I ain't blaming you, Sheriff," John said. "I ain't blaming anyone."

Allen was safe, he thought; that was all that mattered, even though he knew that he would never see the boy again.

John walked toward the path leading to the river. He was going home, he thought, home to the river, where he would be free. He pushed the wet willows aside and walked down the path.

The shantyboat was resting on the water. Some of the boards had been broken where the boat had been washed against the side of the bank by the swift water, but it would not take long to fix them. John looked at the willow where the rope was tied; the bark had been worn off the tree, and he knew how swift the river had been. The river had been kind to him, he thought.

The plank that led to the boat had been washed away; but the shanty was resting next to the bank, close enough for John to step from the bank to the boat. The rope on the tiepost was still there. John stepped into the joeboat and pulled alongside the catfish; and, taking his knife, he cut the fish loose. The fish did not move. John could see where the niblines had cut into its side. He knew that it had been fighting the current.

"Well, go on," John said. "I might change my mind."

The big catfish moved its tail and swam along the sur-

face of the water, then flipped its tail and disappeared.

"I might be after you tomorrow," John holloed.

John walked to the cabin. Limpy scuttled over to him, and he shelled some corn for the duck, rubbing its feathers. He began to pick up the things that had been knocked from the walls of the cabin by the storm. It was good to be home, John thought, as he lay down on the cot.

The sun was high when he awoke. He gathered his line and walked to the joeboat. He bailed out the water and started for the creek to see if he had lost his minnow traps.

John stopped at the creek and tied. He felt something hit him in the back and he looked toward the bank.

Allen stood at the edge of the willows.

"Did the rains hurt your boat, Mr. John?" he asked.

John watched the small boy walk down the bank to the edge of the creek. Tears filled the old man's eyes and he wiped them with his sleeve.

"You better run up the bank," he said.

"Ma knows I'm down here," Allen assured him. "She said to tell you she was sorry and for you to watch me around the water. What is she sorry for, Mr. John?"

John lifted the boy into the boat. The boy put his arms around John's waist.

"I missed you, Mr. John," he said. "I missed Limpy, too."

John shoved the boat from the bank, and he and Allen drifted downriver with the current.